MATHEMATICAL PHYSICS SERIES
Editor: G. Stephenson B.Sc., Ph.D., D.I.C.
Department of Mathematics, Imperial College, London.

AN INTRODUCTION TO NEUTRON TRANSPORT THEORY

An Introduction to Neutron Transport Theory

J. H. TAIT
B.SC., PH.D.

Theoretical Physics Division, A.E.R.E.
Harwell

NEW YORK

AMERICAN ELSEVIER PUBLISHING COMPANY, INC.

© J. H. TAIT, 1964

This edition first published 1965

AMERICAN ELSEVIER PUBLISHING COMPANY, INC.

52 Vanderbilt Avenue,

New York 17, New York

LIBRARY OF CONGRESS CATALOG CARD NUMBER: 65-20005

Made and printed in Great Britain by
Richard Clay (The Chaucer Press), Ltd., Bungay, Suffolk

CONTENTS

Contents

Contents

6. The Neutron Spectrum during Slowing Down in an Infinite Medium

7. Neutron Slowing Down Problems with Spatial Dependence

Contents

8. The Numerical Solution of the Energy Dependent Transport Equation

PREFACE

The purpose of this book is to give an introductory account of the mathematical methods used in neutron transport theory. An attempt has been made to introduce the reader to the practical methods which are available, and where possible the physical significance of various steps in the mathematical arguments has been explained. A number of numerical methods are described which require the use of large digital computers. However, the book is not concerned entirely with a description of such methods, and in the energy independent case several analytical solutions are described. An appendix is devoted to an explanation of the variational method, and examples are given in the text of the use of this method in the calculation of boundary conditions for the diffusion approximation, and in the derivation of the diffusion equation from the transport equation.

The contents of the various chapters are as follows. Chapter 1 is devoted to a description of the physical processes which occur when a neutron collides with the nuclei of the medium in which it is diffusing. In Chapter 2 the neutron transport equation is derived. Chapters 3 and 4 are concerned with the solution of the one velocity group equation and in Chapter 5 the diffusion approximation is discussed. The remaining three chapters are devoted to the solution of the energy dependent equation, commencing with a study of the neutron spectrum during slowing down in an infinite medium. Three topics are then discussed which give an insight into the behaviour of the neutron distribution when there is spatial dependence, i.e. the thermal neutron Milne problem, the age equation and the neutron distribution at large distances from the source. In the final chapter numerical methods and perturbation theory are discussed.

I should like to thank Dr. J. B. Sykes, Dr. G. Rowlands and Dr. J. Perring for reading the manuscript and for their many valuable suggestions. I am indebted to Mr. P. Schofield for his permission to use unpublished work on the thermal neutron Milne problems. Many thanks are due to my wife for her swift typing of the manuscript.

A large number of references has been given for the benefit of the reader who wishes to consult some of the original papers.

J. H. T.

A.E.R.E. Harwell, 1963.

ACKNOWLEDGEMENTS

We are grateful to the following for permission to use copyright material:

The authors and the *Journal of Nuclear Energy* for two tables from 'Some Topics in One-Velocity Neutron Transport Theory' by C. Carter and G. Rowlands from 'Reactor Science and Technology' (*Journal of Nuclear Energy*, Parts A/B) 1961, Vol. 15; the National Research Council of Canada for part of a table from 'The Neutron Density Near a Plane Surface in a Capturing Medium' by J. LeCaine from *Can. J. Res. A*, 28 242 (1950), and the United States Atomic Energy Commission for a table from *Introduction to the Theory of Neutron Diffusion*, Vol. 1, by K. M. Case *et al.*

For permission to redraw diagrams we are indebted to the following:

Atomic Energy of Canada Ltd. for fig. 5.2 from Kushneriuk, A.E.C.L. – 137; Brookhaven National Laboratory for the curves in figs. 1.1, 1.2 from B.N.L. – 325; Oxford University Press for fig 5.1 from Davidson, *Neutron Transport Theory*; Pergamon Press Ltd. for fig. 6.4 from Poole, Nelkin and Stone, Progress in Nuclear Energy, Series I, 130; the Editor, *Physical Review*, for figs. 6.1, 6.2, 6.3 from Placzek, *Phys. Rev.*, **69**, 423.

CHAPTER 1

General Analysis

1.1 Introduction

Neutron transport theory is concerned with the migration of neutrons through media. It is the study of the result of a large number of random, neutron collisions in a medium; one tries to calculate the angular, energy and spatial variations of the neutron distribution in the medium in question. In order to carry out such a calculation the laws governing the individual collisions must be known. These laws can be obtained sometimes from theoretical arguments but in the main are determined experimentally. A brief account of the different types of collision which can occur is given in Section 1.2.

This book is intended to serve as an introduction to neutron transport theory. It does not attempt to describe the mathematical theory with the same rigour as is found in Davison's book [1].

The main application of neutron transport theory is in the study and design of nuclear reactors. The theory of nuclear reactors is based usually on the diffusion approximation. The diffusion equation is obtained from the exact transport equation by approximating to the variation of the neutron distribution with direction. This approximation simplifies the calculation of the spatial variation of the neutron distribution, and gives an accurate description at large distances from all sources and boundaries, that is, at distances large compared with the neutron mean free paths. Therefore, diffusion theory can be used to calculate the overall properties of a large reactor. However, in order to calculate the behaviour of a small system, the diffusion approximation should not be used.

Neutron transport theory is sometimes called neutron diffusion theory: in the context of this book neutron diffusion theory denotes the simplified treatment and not the exact.

Much of the early work on neutron transport theory was concerned with the distribution of neutrons in space and angle rather than in energy, and an approximation was developed in which the energy dependence was removed by integration. This is the constant cross-section approximation, often called one-velocity group theory. It is

1

related to the study which has been made by astrophysicists of radiative transfer in a 'grey' stellar atmosphere. Many of the mathematical problems were solved by them before the neutron was discovered.

In nuclear reactor theory one is vitally interested in the neutron energy distribution, because the probability of the neutron interaction with various nuclei in the reactor often shows considerable variation with energy. However, the study of one velocity group theory does give some insight into the physics, and often the results can be used in the study of problems where the energy variation is important, as these problems can be studied by multi-velocity-group theory in which the velocity range is divided into a number of intervals.

In the chief application of neutron transport theory, namely to reactor design, one is concerned with the energy range from several MeV to about $\frac{1}{40}$ eV.‡ In the theory of neutron shielding, the neutrons which are of interest lie in the high energy tail of the fission spectrum, as these neutrons penetrate to large distances in the shield. In a thermal reactor the majority of the neutrons has an energy of about $\frac{1}{40}$ eV. In some suggested designs of future fast reactors the neutron energy spectrum may be spread over a considerable energy range from 50 eV to several MeV.

Before developing the mathematical theory we shall give a brief description of the various physical processes which occur when a neutron collides with the nuclei of a medium in which the neutrons are migrating.

1.2 Physical processes which occur when a neutron collides with a nucleus

When a neutron collides with a nucleus the following processes can occur:

(i) The neutron can be scattered either elastically or inelastically. In an elastic collision the energy of the neutron will change due to the recoil of the scattering nucleus, but the nuclear state of the latter remains unchanged. In an inelastic collision the scattering nucleus may be excited to an excited state and subsequently decay with the emission of a γ-ray. This often results in a much larger

‡ An eV is the energy gained by an electron in falling through a potential difference of one volt. It is equal to $1 \cdot 602 \times 10^{-12}$ ergs.

2

change of neutron energy than in an elastic collision. This process is particularly important in heavy elements for high energy neutrons.

(ii) The neutron can be captured by the nucleus, which may decay subsequently with the emission of a γ-ray, or a charged particle, for example, an electron.

(iii) The neutron can cause fission on collision with a fissile nucleus, i.e. plutonium, uranium 235, uranium 233 and uranium 238 if the neutron energy is high enough.

There is also a possibility of n, $2n$ collisions in such materials as beryllium and deuterium. However, the number of such events is small compared to other events in, for example, a heavy water moderated reactor.

(a) Cross-section

The probability that a particular process occurs is determined by the neutron cross-section. This can be defined in the following manner. Suppose that a thin sample of material is irradiated by a flux ψ of neutrons per cm² per sec.‡ The number of reactions R_p of a particular process of type p per unit area of the sample is given by

$$R_p = \sigma_p \psi \times \text{number of nuclei/cm}^2 \text{ of the sample,}$$

where σ_p is some proportionality factor and is called the cross-section. The number of reactions per unit volume of the sample is equal to R_p/d, where d is the thickness of the sample, and this is given by

$$R_p/d = \sigma_p \psi n,$$

where n is the number of nuclei per c.c. Cross-sections are measured in barns; one barn is equal to 10^{-24} cm².

The product $n\sigma_p$ is called the macroscopic cross-section and is denoted by Σ_p. The probability that a neutron will collide with a

‡ The flux of neutrons $\psi(\Omega)$ travelling in a direction Ω is defined as the number of neutrons passing through unit area perpendicular to Ω per second. The total flux ϕ is defined as the integral of ψ over all directions Ω, i.e.

$$\phi = \int \psi(\Omega) \, d\Omega$$

3

nucleus of the medium on travelling a distance dx producing a process p is therefore

$$dx\Sigma_p = dx/l_p,$$

where $$l_p = \Sigma_p^{-1};$$

l_p is called the neutron mean free path for the process p.

The variation of some neutron cross-sections with energy is illustrated in Figs. 1.1 and 1.2.

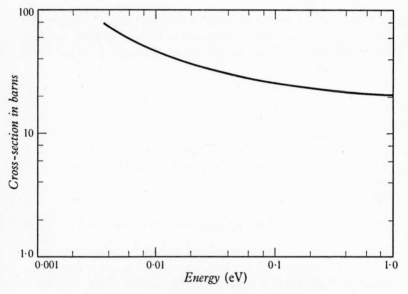

Fig. 1.1. Total scattering cross-section for hydrogen

It can be seen that in some cases there is a smooth variation of cross-section with energy; in other cases the cross-section fluctuates violently. The resonance structure in the latter case is due to the fact that the neutron combines with the nucleus to form a compound state, which may disintegrate in various ways. If the resonances are very close together inadequate resolution of the apparatus may result in an experimental curve which is smooth.

The resonance absorption of a neutron by a nucleus of atomic weight A may result in a single excited state of the isotope of atomic weight $A + 1$. The energy level of this excited state is broadened by

4

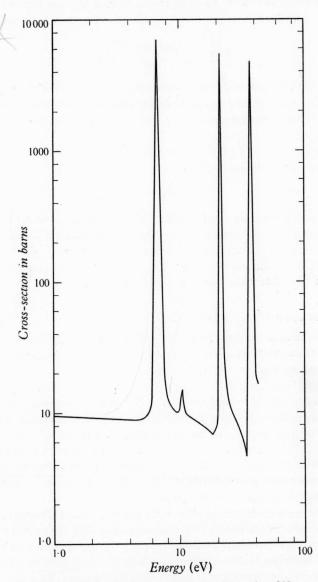

Fig. 1.2. Neutron capture cross-section in uranium 238

the finite lifetime of the state. Breit and Wigner [2] have shown that
the formula for the cross-section at such a resonance is given by

$$\sigma(E) = \frac{\frac{1}{4}\sigma_0 \Gamma^2 (E/E_R)^{\frac{1}{2}}}{(E - E_R)^2 + \frac{1}{4}\Gamma^2} \tag{1}$$

where $\sigma(E)$ denotes the total cross-section, i.e. the sum of the resonance scattering and the resonance capture cross-section. σ_0 is the peak
value of the sum of the scattering and capture cross-sections at the
energy E_R.

The width Γ_i for a particular process i is related to the disintegration constant α_i by the formula

$$\Gamma_i = \hbar \alpha_i,$$

where $2\pi\hbar$ is Planck's constant, and the disintegration constant α_i is
the inverse of the lifetime of the compound nucleus for a disintegra-
tion of type i. The capture cross-section σ_c is given by $\sigma_c = (\Gamma_c/\Gamma)\sigma(E)$,
and the scattering cross-section by $\sigma_{sc} = (\Gamma_n/\Gamma)\sigma(E)$, where Γ_c and
Γ_n are the capture and neutron widths respectively.

(b) Discussion of various processes

Let us consider the three processes—scattering, capture and fission.

There are two types of scattering. First there is resonance scattering
in which the neutron combines with the scattering nucleus to form a
compound state, which then disintegrates into the original particles.
The second type is called 'potential scattering', and here the neutron
is merely deflected without the formation of a compound state. In the
region of a resonance, the resonance scattering is much larger than
the potential scattering. The two processes can interfere with each
other with the result that the cross-section might decrease before a
resonance and increase after it. The cross-section for potential scattering is largely independent of energy.

In the inelastic scattering process the neutron excites the scattering
nucleus which then decays to the ground state with the emission of
a γ-ray. This process is an important one in the slowing down of
fission neutrons in heavy elements; it is the major cause of the
degradation of the neutron energy in a fast reactor. It would be
impossible to give a survey of all the experimental data on this subject. However, in Chapter 8, multi-velocity group theory is discussed

and references are given of the literature where constants incorporating all the latest inelastic data can be found.

The scattering of neutrons whose energy is near to thermal will be influenced by the chemical binding of the scattering nucleus in the particular compound considered.‡ Various theoretical models have been proposed to give the inelastic scattering cross-sections and data is becoming available from the Chalk River Scattering Project [3]. In this project the quantity $\Sigma(E' \longrightarrow E, \theta)$ is measured for various moderators, where Σ is the cross-section for scattering from an energy E' to energy E through an angle θ. The chemical binding is the reason why the hydrogen scattering cross-section increases near to thermal energies. This cross-section is plotted in Fig. 1.1.

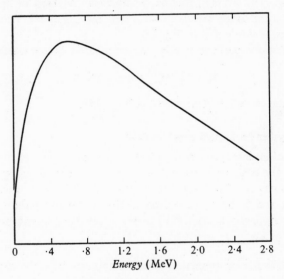

Fig. 1.3. Fission spectrum

Let us now consider the capture cross-section. If one averages the resonance formula over many resonances [4], one obtains a formula of the following type:

$$[\sigma_c(E)]_{Av} = \frac{a\Gamma_c}{E^{\frac{1}{2}}(\Gamma_c + bE^{\frac{1}{2}})},$$

‡ At a temperature of 0° C. the energy of a neutron is approximately $\frac{1}{40}$ eV.

where a and b are constants. Depending on the value of the capture width Γ_c compared with the other quantities, the average cross-section $[\sigma_c]_{Av}$ may or may not show a $E^{-\frac{1}{2}}$ variation with energy. For some elements, e.g. boron, the capture cross-section shows a $E^{-\frac{1}{2}}$ variation over a large energy range.

A neutron can cause fission in certain heavy elements. The nucleus after the absorption of the neutron is left in a highly excited state. It may then undergo fission, i.e. split into two approximately equal parts. The fission is accompanied by the release of secondary neutrons. Uranium 235 and certain plutonium isotopes are fissile to low energy neutrons; uranium 238 is fissile to neutrons above 1 MeV; and other elements, for example bismuth, are fissile to higher energy neutrons. The average number of neutrons released on fission depends on the fissile material and is between 2·5 and 3. Their energy spectrum is illustrated in Fig. 1.3.

The fission spectrum is given approximately by the expression

$$\sinh (2·29E)^{\frac{1}{2}} \exp (-E/0·965),$$

where the energy E is measured in MeV [5].

1.3 Doppler broadened cross-sections

One is often interested in the effect which the motion of the nucleus has on the neutron cross-section, when the neutron energy is near to a resonance. The resonance becomes Doppler broadened.

Let $\mathbf{v}$ and $\mathbf{V}$ be the velocities of the neutron and the absorbing nucleus respectively. Let $P(\mathbf{V})$ be the normalized distribution of $\mathbf{V}$, i.e. $\int P(\mathbf{V})d^3\mathbf{V} = 1$.

The effective cross-section is then computed from the relation

$$v\sigma_{\text{eff}}(v) = \int |\mathbf{v} - \mathbf{V}|\, \sigma(|\mathbf{v} - \mathbf{V}|)P(\mathbf{V})d^3\mathbf{V}, \tag{2}$$

where $\sigma(|\mathbf{v} - \mathbf{V}|)$ is the cross-section as a function of the relative velocity, $\mathbf{v} - \mathbf{V}$, of the neutron and the nucleus. $P(\mathbf{V})$ is given by a Maxwellian distribution of velocities, i.e.

$$P(\mathbf{V})d^3\mathbf{V} = (M/2\pi kT)^{\frac{3}{2}} \exp (-MV^2/2kT)4\pi V^2 dV, \tag{3}$$

where T is the temperature, k is Boltzmann's constant and M is the mass of the scattering nucleus.

8

Noting that the ratio V/v is small for most resonances of interest, it can be shown that the integral reduces to the following for the cross-section $\sigma(E)$ given by the Breit–Wigner formula:

$$\sigma(x, \zeta) = \frac{\sigma_0}{4\pi\zeta} \int_{-\infty}^{+\infty} (1 + y)^{-2} \exp\left[-(x - y)^2/4\zeta\right]dy, \qquad (4)$$

where
$$\zeta = \frac{4E_R mkT}{M\Gamma^2},$$

and
$$x = \frac{E - E_R}{\frac{1}{2}\Gamma},$$

m is the neutron mass. The ratio M/m is equal to the atomic weight A of the nucleus, and (4) was originally obtained by Bethe and Placzek [6]. Hinman and Sampson [7] have discussed refinements of the original treatment. However, the improvement from the more rigorous treatment turns out to be of minor practical importance.

1.4 The scattering law for elastic collisions between neutrons and nuclei

(a) Slowing down mechanisms

A neutron can lose energy in a medium as the result of elastic and inelastic collisions with the nuclei in the medium. If the energy of the neutron is less than the energy difference between the first excited state and the ground state of the nucleus, then the neutron will lose energy only as the result of elastic collisions with the nucleus, i.e. as in a billiard ball collision. This is the principal mechanism for the slowing down of fission neutrons in materials such as graphite, water, etc. These materials are known as moderators.

In order to derive a scattering law the following assumptions are made:

(i) The atomic nuclei with which the neutrons collide are initially at rest.

(ii) The nuclei recoil freely after a collision.

The neutron cannot be considered as a rigid sphere at all energies. Let λ be the de Broglie wave length of neutron.‡ Then

$$\lambda^{-1} = p/h = 3\cdot5 \cdot 10^{11}(E)^{\frac{1}{2}} \text{ cm.}^{-1},$$

where p is the momentum of the neutron, h is Planck's constant and the energy E is measured in MeV.

‡ A moving particle has associated with it a wave motion and this has a definite wave length given by $\lambda = h/p$.

Let a be the radius of a nucleus of atomic weight A, i.e.

$$a \sim (1{\cdot}47)10^{-13} A^{\frac{1}{3}} \text{ (see [4])}.$$

Then
$$a/\lambda = 0{\cdot}323 A^{\frac{1}{3}} E^{\frac{1}{2}}, \text{ where } 2\pi\, \bar{\lambda} = \lambda.$$

If $\bar{\lambda} > a$ then $E < 10 A^{-\frac{2}{3}}$. In this case it is impossible to say at what angle the neutron hits the nucleus; the scattering should be isotropic in the centre of the mass system. For heavy nuclei, i.e. $A = 200$, the scattering should be approximately isotropic in the centre of mass system for energies up to 100 keV. For lighter nuclei the energy range is much larger. The scattering which we have been discussing is the potential scattering.

To formulate the problem mathematically the Schrödinger equation describing the collision between the neutron and the nucleus is considered. The potential between the neutron and the nucleus depends on the relative co-ordinates and therefore the wave equation can be written in terms of these relative co-ordinates and those of the centre of mass. The wave function for the complete system is then the product of the two functions. One factor represents the relative motion of the neutron and the nucleus, and is the same as that describing the motion of a neutron with reduced mass $A/(A + 1)$ in the field of the nucleus. The second function describes the motion of the centre of mass of the neutron and nucleus.

The angular distribution $g(\theta_1, E_1)$ of scattered neutrons in the centre of mass system, i.e. that in which the centre of mass is stationary, is given by

$$g(\theta_1, E_1) = \left(\frac{1}{4\pi}\right)[1 + 3g_1(E_1)P_1(\cos \theta_1) + \ldots],$$

where θ_1 is the scattering angle and E_1 the energy of relative motion in the centre of mass system. The second term in this series will be small when $\bar{\lambda} > a$.

(b) Derivation of various relations

To obtain relations between the energy before and after the collision the equations for the conservation of energy and momentum in the laboratory system are considered. These relations have been obtained by many authors, e.g. Marshak [8]. Let v' and the vector Ω' be the velocity and the direction of the neutron before collision, and v and Ω the corresponding values after the collision.

10

Let v_A and Ω_A be the velocity and the direction of the scattering nucleus after the collision; it is assumed to be at rest before the collision.

From the conservation of momentum

$$v'\Omega' = v\Omega + v_A\Omega_A A. \tag{5}$$

From the conservation of energy

$$\tfrac{1}{2}(v')^2 = \tfrac{1}{2}v^2 + \tfrac{1}{2}Av_A^2. \tag{6}$$

From (5)

$$A^2v_A^2 = (v')^2 + v^2 - 2vv'\Omega \cdot \Omega'. \tag{7}$$

Eliminating v_A between (6) and (7) then

$$(v')^2 - v^2 = A^{-1}[(v')^2 + v^2 - 2vv'\mu], \tag{8}$$

where $\mu = \Omega \cdot \Omega'$, i.e. μ is the cosine of the angle between Ω and Ω'.

Therefore $\quad \mu = \tfrac{1}{2}[(A+1)(v/v') - (A-1)(v'/v)]. \tag{9}$

The velocity of the neutron in the centre of mass system before the collision $(v'\Omega')_{\text{cms}}$ is given by

$$(v'\Omega')_{\text{cms}} = Av'\Omega'/(A+1).$$

After the collision

$$(v\Omega)_{\text{cms}} = v\Omega - v'\Omega'/(A+1).$$

Let μ_1 be the cosine of the angle of scatter in the centre of mass system.

Then

$$\mu_1 = \frac{(v'\Omega' \cdot v\Omega)_{\text{cms}}}{(v'v)_{\text{cms}}} = \frac{vv'\Omega \cdot \Omega' - (v')^2/(A+1)}{v'[v^2 + (v')^2/(A+1)^2 - 2vv'\Omega \cdot \Omega'/(A+1)]^{\frac{1}{2}}},$$

$$= \frac{\tfrac{1}{2}(A+1)v^2 - \tfrac{1}{2}(v')^2(A^2+1)/(A+1)}{A(v')^2/(A+1)}. \tag{10}$$

Eliminating v/v' between (9) and (10) the following relation is obtained between μ and μ_1:

$$\mu = \frac{A\mu_1 + 1}{[1 + 2\mu_1 A + A^2]^{\frac{1}{2}}}. \tag{11}$$

11

(c) *The case of spherically symmetrical scattering in the centre of mass system*

In the case of spherically symmetrical scattering the probability that a neutron will be scattered through an angle lying in the range θ_1 to $\theta_1 + d\theta_1$ is given by

$$\tfrac{1}{2} \sin \theta_1 \, d\theta_1 = -\tfrac{1}{2} \, d\mu_1,$$

i.e. equal intervals of μ_1 have equal probabilities.

From (10) it can be seen that

$$d\mu_1 = \frac{(A + 1)^2 \, dE}{2AE'}.$$

(The energy $E = \tfrac{1}{2}mv^2$.)

Therefore, equal intervals of μ_1 correspond to equal intervals of the final energy of the neutron. The energy E of the neutron after the collision will be distributed with equal probability between E' and a minimum value given by (10) for $\mu_1 = -1$.

When
$$\mu_1 = -1,$$

$$E = \frac{(A - 1)^2 E'}{(A + 1)^2} = (1 - q)E',$$

where
$$q = \frac{4A}{(1 + A)^2}.$$

The probability that a neutron of energy E' is scattered into the energy interval E to $E + dE$ is

$$dE/qE' \quad \text{for} \quad E' > E > E'(1 - q),$$

and is zero outside this energy range.

The average of the cosine of the angle of scatter is given as follows:

$$\bar{\mu} = \tfrac{1}{2} \int_{-1}^{+1} \mu \, d\mu_1,$$

$$= \tfrac{1}{2} \int_{-1}^{+1} \frac{A\mu_1 + 1}{[A^2 + 2A\mu_1 + 1]^{\frac{1}{2}}} \, d\mu_1 = \tfrac{2}{3}A. \tag{12}$$

It has been shown that in an elastic collision the energy loss is a percentage of the initial energy. It is convenient, therefore, in neutron slowing down problems to use the lethargy variable u. This is defined as follows

$$u = \ln (E_0/E),$$

where E_0 is some arbitrary neutron energy. The change in lethargy of a neutron when it collides with a nucleus is independent of its energy.

The average lethargy loss ξ in a collision with a nucleus of atomic weight A is given by

$$\xi = \int_{E'(1-q)}^{E'} [\ln (E_0/E) - \ln (E_0/E')] \frac{dE}{qE'},$$

$$= 1 + \frac{(1-q)}{q} \ln (1-q),$$

$$= 1 + \frac{(A-1)^2}{4A} \ln (1-q). \tag{13}$$

The following table gives the value of q, ξ and $\bar{\mu}$ for hydrogen, deuterium, beryllium and carbon.

Nucleus	q	ξ	$\bar{\mu}$	N_c
H	1·000	1·000	0·667	18
D	0·889	0·725	0·333	25
Be	0·360	0·209	0·074	86
C	0·284	0·158	0·056	114

With the values of ξ given in the table the number of collisions N_c required to slow a neutron from 2MeV to $\frac{1}{40}$ eV (thermal energies) can be estimated. The value of N_c is given in the last column of the table for the different moderators.

(d) The scattering law when the scattering nucleus is initially at rest

In order to develop the theory in later chapters, an expression will be required for the probability that a neutron of velocity v' and proceeding in a direction Ω', is scattered into the velocity range v to $v + dv$, and into the elementary cone $d\Omega$ surrounding Ω.

Formula (8) relates the velocities of the neutron before and after

13

the collision with the cosine of the angle of scatter μ. Therefore, the transfer function will contain the following factor

$$\delta[\mu - \tfrac{1}{2}(A + 1)(v/v') + \tfrac{1}{2}(A - 1)(v'/v)], \tag{14}$$

$\delta(x - x_0)$ is the Dirac delta function. $\delta(x - x_0)$ is zero except for $x = x_0$ and $\int \delta(x - x_0)\, dx = 1$.

In the case of spherically symmetrical scattering it was shown that all permissible values of v^2 are equally likely. The probability of scattering into the velocity range v to $v + dv$ is therefore proportional to

$$d(v^2) = 2v\, dv. \tag{15}$$

Let $f_e(v', \mathbf{\Omega}' \longrightarrow v, \mathbf{\Omega})\, dv\, d\Omega$ be the probability that a neutron of velocity v' and travelling in a direction $\mathbf{\Omega}'$ is scattered into a velocity interval v to $v + dv$ and into the cone $d\Omega$ around $\mathbf{\Omega}$.
Then f_e contains the two factors (14) and (15), i.e.

$$f_e = Cv\delta[\mu - \tfrac{1}{2}(A + 1)(v/v') + \tfrac{1}{2}(A - 1)(v'/v)], \tag{16}$$

where C is a normalizing constant determined from the condition

$$\int\int f_e(v', \mathbf{\Omega}' \longrightarrow v, \mathbf{\Omega})\, dv\, d\Omega = 1.$$

It can be shown easily that

$$C = \frac{(A + 1)^2}{4\pi A(v')^2}. \tag{17}$$

f_e is zero outside the range $v' \geqslant v \geqslant v'(A - 1)/(A + 1)$.

(e) *The scattering law when the scattering nucleus has an initial motion*

If the scattering nucleus has an initial velocity v_A' and is travelling in the direction $\mathbf{\Omega}_A'$, then the scattering law can be written in the following way

$$f_e(v', \mathbf{\Omega}' \longrightarrow v, \mathbf{\Omega})\, d\omega\, d\Omega^0$$

$$= \frac{(A + 1)^2}{4\pi A^2} \frac{\omega}{v_r^2} \delta\!\left[\mathbf{s} \cdot \mathbf{s}' - \frac{A + 1}{2A} \cdot \frac{\omega}{v_r}\right] d\omega\, d\Omega^0, \tag{18}$$

14

where $\qquad v_r\mathbf{s}' = v_A'\mathbf{\Omega}_A' - v'\mathbf{\Omega}',$

and $\qquad \omega\mathbf{s} = v\mathbf{\Omega} - v'\mathbf{\Omega}'.$

$\mathbf{s}, \mathbf{s}'$ are unit vectors; v_r is the initial velocity of the scattering nucleus relative to the neutron; and ω the velocity of the neutron after the collision relative to its motion before the collision. $d\Omega^0$ is an element of solid angle in a co-ordinate system in which the neutron was originally at rest.

CHAPTER 2

The Equations of Neutron Transport Theory

2.1 Neutron transport equation

The neutron density N in a medium is a function of the position denoted by the vector $\mathbf{r}$, the direction of the neutron $\boldsymbol{\Omega}$, its velocity v and the time t.‡

Let $N(\mathbf{r}, v, \boldsymbol{\Omega}, t) \, dv \, d\Omega$ be the number of neutrons per unit volume at the point P with velocities in the range v to $v + dv$ and directions lying in the elementary cone $d\Omega$ about $\boldsymbol{\Omega}$, at time t.

The neutron density N in a volume element dV at $\mathbf{r}$ can change due to three effects.

   (i) Neutrons can stream through the volume element without collision.

   (ii) Neutrons can undergo collisions in the volume element and can change their energy and direction.

   (iii) It can change due to the presence of sources in dV.

Let us consider the change in the number of neutrons in the volume element dV due to streaming.

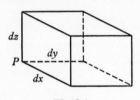

Fig. 2.1

$vN(\mathbf{r}, v, \boldsymbol{\Omega}, t)$ is the number of neutrons of velocity v crossing unit area perpendicular to $\boldsymbol{\Omega}$ per unit time at t. The number of neutrons flowing through a unit area, whose normal makes an angle $\cos^{-1} \mu$ with $\boldsymbol{\Omega}$ is equal to $v\mu N$.

The number of neutrons, travelling in direction $\boldsymbol{\Omega}$ of velocity v, flowing into the elementary volume $dV(= dx \, dy \, dz)$ at P (see Fig. 2.1) is therefore

$$v\Omega_x N(x, y, z) \, dy \, dz + v\Omega_y N(x, y, z) \, dx \, dz + v\Omega_z N(x, y, z) \, dx \, dy.$$

‡ It is sometimes convenient to consider N as a function of the energy E or lethargy $\ln (E_0/E)$ instead of the velocity v. It depends on the particular problem. The reader should consult Appendix A for information regarding the relation between the velocity, energy and lethargy scales.

The number leaving is equal to

$$v\Omega_x N(x + dx, y, z)\, dy\, dz + v\Omega_y N(x, y + dy, z)\, dx\, dz$$
$$+ v\Omega_z N(x, y, z + dz)\, dx\, dy.$$

The loss due to streaming is the difference of these last two expressions and is equal to

$$\left[v\Omega_x \frac{\partial N}{\partial x} + v\Omega_y \frac{\partial N}{\partial y} + v\Omega_z \frac{\partial N}{\partial z} \right] dV = v\mathbf{\Omega} \cdot \operatorname{grad} N\, dV. \tag{1}$$

Let us consider now the collisions which occur per unit time in the volume element. Let $\Sigma(v)$ be the total macroscopic cross-section for all processes; $\Sigma(v)$ is the inverse mean free path. Let $c(v)$ be the mean number of secondary neutrons produced per collision. The quantity $c(v)\Sigma(v)$ is the mean number of secondaries per unit path.

Let $c(v')f(v', \mathbf{\Omega}' \longrightarrow v, \mathbf{\Omega})\, dv\, d\Omega$ be the mean number of neutrons produced in the velocity range dv and cone $d\Omega$ when a neutron of velocity v' and direction $\mathbf{\Omega}'$ undergoes a collision with a stationary nucleus. The form of the expression $f(v', \mathbf{\Omega}' \longrightarrow v, \mathbf{\Omega})$ for elastic scattering was considered in Section 1.4 (d).

In the elementary volume dV, the number of neutrons of velocity v and travelling in direction $\mathbf{\Omega}$ which undergo collisions is equal to

$$v\Sigma(v)N(\mathbf{r}, v, \mathbf{\Omega}, t)\, dv\, d\Omega\, dV. \tag{2}$$

This follows immediately from the definition of the mean free path. The $N\, dv\, d\Omega\, dV$ neutrons in dV move a distance $v\, dt$ in time dt and the number of collisions per unit time is given by the above formula.

The number of neutrons, of other velocities and travelling in other directions, which are scattered into the velocity range v to $v + dv$ and direction $\mathbf{\Omega}$ is equal to

$$dv\, d\Omega\, dV \int\!\!\int v'c(v')\Sigma(v')f(v', \mathbf{\Omega}' \longrightarrow v, \mathbf{\Omega})N(\mathbf{r}, v', \mathbf{\Omega}', t)\, dv'\, d\Omega'. \tag{3}$$

Let $S(\mathbf{r}, v, \mathbf{\Omega}, t)$ be the source strength of neutrons in the particular volume element. $S\, dv\, d\Omega\, dV$ is the number of neutrons emitted by the sources in the volume element dV at $\mathbf{r}$ in the cone $d\Omega$ and in the velocity range v to $v + dv$.

The rate of change of $N(\mathbf{r}, v, \mathbf{\Omega}, t)$ with time is equal to the number of neutrons scattered to the velocity v and direction $\mathbf{\Omega}$ from other directions and velocities less the loss due to leakage and scattering out of v and Ω.

The transport equation is therefore

$$\frac{\partial N(\mathbf{r}, v, \Omega, t)}{\partial t} = -v\Omega \cdot \text{grad } N(\mathbf{r}, v, \Omega, t) - v\Sigma(v)N(\mathbf{r}, v, \Omega, t)$$

$$+ \iint v'c(v')\Sigma(v')f(v', \Omega' \longrightarrow v, \Omega)N(\mathbf{r}, v', \Omega', t) \, dv' \, d\Omega'$$
$$+ S(\mathbf{r}, v, \Omega, t). \quad (4)$$

The forms of Σ, c and f are now considered for the various types of collision which a neutron can undergo. Let σ_e, σ_{in}, σ_f and σ_c denote the cross-sections for elastic scattering, inelastic scattering, fission and capture. These processes were described in Chapter 1. If there are n nuclei per unit volume

$$\Sigma = l^{-1} = n(\sigma_e + \sigma_{in} + \sigma_f + \sigma_c), \quad (5)$$

and $$c\Sigma = n(\sigma_e + \sigma_{in} + \nu\sigma_f), \quad (6)$$

where ν is the probable number of neutrons per fission.

The expression for $c(v')f(v', \Omega' \longrightarrow v, \Omega)$ is

$$\nu p_f f_f + p_{in} f_{in} + p_e f_e, \quad (7)$$

where p_f, p_{in} and p_e are the probabilities for fission, inelastic scattering and elastic scattering in a collision.

$\nu f_f(v', \Omega' \longrightarrow v, \Omega) \, dv \, d\Omega$ is the probable number of neutrons produced in the velocity interval dv and cone $d\Omega$ from the fission of a nucleus by a neutron of velocity v' travelling in the direction Ω'. In fission, the neutrons are emitted isotropically; ν and the fission spectrum $G(v)$ are assumed to be independent of v' (they do show some variations with v' at higher energies). Therefore

$$\nu f_f(v', \Omega' \longrightarrow v, \Omega) = \nu G(v)/4\pi. \quad (8)$$

$f_{in}(v', \Omega' \longrightarrow v, \Omega) \, dv \, d\Omega$ is the probable number of neutrons produced in the velocity interval dv and cone $d\Omega$ when a neutron of velocity v' and direction Ω' is scattered inelastically by a nucleus. The neutron is absorbed by the scattering nucleus, and is then emitted isotropically at a lower energy; thus

$$f_{in}(v', \Omega' \longrightarrow v, \Omega) = f_{in}(v' \longrightarrow v)/4\pi, \quad (9)$$

where $f_{in}(v' \longrightarrow v) \, dv$ is the probability that the neutron is scattered into the velocity interval dv.

All other scattering processes, i.e. those in which the nucleus is left in its original state, are included in f_e. The form of f_e for this type of collision when the scattering is isotropic in the centre-of-mass system has been given in Chapter 1. The scattering is only isotropic in the centre-of-mass system for light nuclei if the neutron energy is less than several MeV, and for heavy nuclei if the neutron energy is less than several hundred keV. It may still be anisotropic below these energies for resonance scattering. Often the experimental information about the angular distribution in the centre-of-mass system for resonance scattering is scanty. When the scattering nucleus is very heavy, the energy loss is small and often can be neglected. Because the detailed angular distribution $f_e(\mathbf{\Omega'} \longrightarrow \mathbf{\Omega})$ is not known, the scattering is assumed to be isotropic and the scattering cross-section σ_s is replaced by σ_{tr}, where

$$\sigma_{tr} = \sigma_s\left[1 - \int_{-1}^{+1} \mu f_e(\mu) \, d\mu\right], \tag{10}$$

and where μ is the cosine of the angle between the initial and final directions of the neutron, i.e. $\mu = \mathbf{\Omega} \cdot \mathbf{\Omega'}$. σ_{tr} is called the transport cross-section. The quantity $\int_{-1}^{+1} \mu f_e(\mu) \, d\mu$ is provided by experimental measurement. This transport approximation is discussed in later chapters.

2.2 Integral equation

If the scattering is isotropic, the right-hand side of the Boltzmann equation (4) simplifies as the term $f(v', \mathbf{\Omega'} \longrightarrow v, \mathbf{\Omega})$ has no angular dependence. The integral on the right-hand side of (4) reduces to

$$\frac{1}{4\pi}\int v'c(v')\Sigma(v')f(v' \longrightarrow v)N_0(\mathbf{r}, v') \, dv', \tag{11}$$

where $f(v' \longrightarrow v)$ is the probability that a neutron of velocity is scattered into the velocity range v to $v + dv$, and $N_0(\mathbf{r}, v') = \int N(\mathbf{r}, v', \mathbf{\Omega'}) \, d\Omega'$ is the density of neutrons at $\mathbf{r}$.

In the case of isotropic scattering it is possible to derive an integral equation for the density $N_0(\mathbf{r}, v')$. This can be achieved by the integration of (4) or it can be obtained from first principles. The latter derivation will be given as it is instructive from a physical point of view.

The cross-sections will be assumed to be independent of position in the medium, and the medium is bounded by a convex surface so that a path between two points always lies in the medium.

Consider the contributions to the neutron flux at a point P due to neutrons which originate from a point P', and travel direct to P without a collision (see Fig. 2.2).

Let the volume element dV at P subtend a solid angle $d\Omega$ at P'.

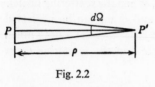

Fig. 2.2

The volume element dV at P is therefore equal to $\rho^2 \, d\rho \, d\Omega$, where ρ is the distance between P and P'. It will be assumed that the source neutrons $S(\mathbf{r'}, v)$ are emitted isotropically at $\mathbf{r'}$.

The number of neutrons of velocity v travelling in the direction Ω in the cone $d\Omega$ due to sources and scattering collisions in a volume element dV' at P' is equal to

$$(d\Omega/4\pi)\left[S(\mathbf{r'}, v) + \int v' \Sigma_s(v') f(v' \longrightarrow v) N_0(\mathbf{r'}, v') \, dv' \right] dV'. \quad (12)$$

The probability that these neutrons travel from P' to P without a collision is equal to $\exp[-\rho\Sigma]$, where Σ is the total macroscopic cross-section.

Now the cross-sectional area dA of the cone $d\Omega$ at P is equal to $\rho^2 \, d\Omega$.

The flux of neutrons at P travelling in the direction Ω and arriving at time t is equal to

$$(dV'/4\pi\rho^2) \exp(-\rho\Sigma)$$

$$\left[S(\mathbf{r'}, v, t - \rho/v) + \int v' \Sigma_s(v') f(v' \longrightarrow v) N_0(\mathbf{r'}, v', t - \rho/v) \, dv' \right]. \quad (13)$$

The neutrons take a time ρ/v to travel from P' to P.

Integrating over all directions Ω, the following equation is obtained for $vN_0(\mathbf{r}, v)$:

$$vN_0(\mathbf{r}, v, t) = \int \frac{\exp(-\rho\Sigma)}{4\pi\rho^2} \left[S(\mathbf{r'}, v, t - \rho/v) \right.$$

$$\left. + \int v' \Sigma_s(v') f(v' \longrightarrow v) N_0(\mathbf{r'}, v', t - \rho/v) \, dv' \right] dV'. \quad (14)$$

2.3 The Adjoint equation

If the neutron distribution does not vary with time then $N(\mathbf{r}, v, \boldsymbol{\Omega})$ satisfies the equation

$$v\boldsymbol{\Omega} \cdot \operatorname{grad} N(\mathbf{r}, v, \boldsymbol{\Omega}) + v\Sigma(v)N(\mathbf{r}, v, \boldsymbol{\Omega})$$
$$= \iint v'c(v')\Sigma(v')f(v', \boldsymbol{\Omega}' \longrightarrow v, \boldsymbol{\Omega})N(\mathbf{r}, v', \boldsymbol{\Omega}')\, dv'\, d\Omega \\ + S(\mathbf{r}, v, \boldsymbol{\Omega}). \quad (15)$$

If there is a solution of this equation in the absence of external sources $S(\mathbf{r}, v, \boldsymbol{\Omega})$ then the resulting homogeneous equation describes the neutron distribution in a system where there is a balance between the neutron production due to fission and the losses due to capture and leakage from the system. In the system a self-sustaining chain reaction is proceeding, and the system is said to be in a critical state. The system is said to be sub-critical if losses out-number production, i.e. the neutron density decreases with time. The system is super-critical if the reverse occurs and the neutron density increases with time. Generally (15) does not have a solution and the following modified equation is considered:

$$v\boldsymbol{\Omega} \cdot \operatorname{grad} N(\mathbf{r}, v\boldsymbol{\Omega}) + (\alpha + v\Sigma)N(\mathbf{r}, v, \boldsymbol{\Omega})$$
$$= \iint v'c(v')\Sigma(v')f(v', \boldsymbol{\Omega}' \longrightarrow v, \boldsymbol{\Omega})N(\mathbf{r}, v', \boldsymbol{\Omega}')\, dv'\, d\Omega', \quad (16)$$

where α is a constant. This equation has solutions for certain values of the constant α, denoted by α_i. The eigen values α_i depend on the geometry and composition of the medium. The corresponding solution of (16) for an eigen value α_i will be denoted by $N_i(\mathbf{r}, v, \boldsymbol{\Omega})$. The functions $N_i(\mathbf{r}, v, \boldsymbol{\Omega})$ satisfy the geometrical boundary conditions, i.e. at the boundary between two media $N_i(\mathbf{r}, v, \boldsymbol{\Omega})$ must be continuous and at a free surface $N_i(\mathbf{r}, v, \boldsymbol{\Omega})$ must be zero for all incoming directions. The constant α could have been introduced as a factor multiplying $c(v')$. However, it is more convenient to introduce it as in (16); it will be shown that α is the time constant of the non-critical system. Assuming that the functions $N_i(\mathbf{r}, v, \boldsymbol{\Omega})$ are a complete set, the time dependent solution of (4) can be expanded in terms of these functions.

It can be shown easily that the following series is a general solution of (4):

$$N(\mathbf{r}, v, \boldsymbol{\Omega}, t) = \sum_i a_i N_i(\mathbf{r}, v, \boldsymbol{\Omega}) \exp(\alpha_i t). \quad (17)$$

For large t the solution is given by

$$N_0(\mathbf{r}, v, \mathbf{\Omega}) \exp(\alpha_0 t),$$

where α_0 is the maximum value of the α_i's. The system is subcritical, critical or supercritical depending on whether α_0 is negative, zero or positive. The coefficients a_i of the series are determined from the boundary conditions which may be specified at some particular time.

The functions $N_i(\mathbf{r}, v, \mathbf{\Omega})$ in the velocity dependent case do not comprise an orthogonal set. To determine the coefficients of the series (17) for example, the set of functions $N_j\dagger(\mathbf{r}, v, \mathbf{\Omega})$ to which they are orthogonal must be specified.

The functions $N_j\dagger(\mathbf{r}, v, \mathbf{\Omega})$ satisfy the equation

$$-v\mathbf{\Omega}.\ \text{grad}\ N_j\dagger(\mathbf{r}, v, \mathbf{\Omega}) + (\alpha_j + v\Sigma)N_j\dagger(\mathbf{r}, v, \mathbf{\Omega})$$
$$= \int\!\!\int vc(v)\Sigma(v)f(v, \mathbf{\Omega} \longrightarrow v', \mathbf{\Omega}')N_j\dagger(\mathbf{r}, v', \mathbf{\Omega}')\ dv'\ d\Omega'. \quad (18)$$

If (16) is multiplied by $N_j\dagger(\mathbf{r}, v, \mathbf{\Omega})$ and (18) by $N_i(\mathbf{r}, v, \mathbf{\Omega})$ and the two equations subtracted then the following orthogonality relation is easily proved

$$(\alpha_i - \alpha_j)\int\!\!\int\!\!\int N_i(\mathbf{r}, v, \mathbf{\Omega})N_j\dagger(\mathbf{r}, v, \mathbf{\Omega})\ dv\ d\Omega\ dV = 0.$$

The $N_j\dagger(\mathbf{r}, v, \mathbf{\Omega})$ satisfy a different boundary condition at a free surface, namely

$$N_j\dagger(\mathbf{r}, v, \mathbf{\Omega}) = 0,$$

for all outgoing directions $\mathbf{\Omega}$.

The adjoint equation is needed for the development of perturbation theory and the variational method. Perturbation theory is discussed in Chapter 8, and the variational method in Appendix B. The reader should consult the Appendix for a definition of adjoint.

CHAPTER 3

One Group Theory

3.1 One velocity group theory equation

Consider the time dependent transport equation (Chapter 2, equation (4))

$$\frac{\partial N(\mathbf{r}, v, \mathbf{\Omega}, t)}{\partial t} = -v\mathbf{\Omega} \cdot \text{grad } N(\mathbf{r}, v, \mathbf{\Omega}, t) - v\Sigma N(\mathbf{r}, v, \mathbf{\Omega}, t)$$

$$+ \iint v'c(v')\Sigma(v')f(v', \mathbf{\Omega}' \longrightarrow v, \mathbf{\Omega})N(\mathbf{r}, v', \mathbf{\Omega}', t) \, dv' \, d\Omega'$$

$$+ S(\mathbf{r}, v, \mathbf{\Omega}, t). \quad (1)$$

If all the neutrons have the same velocity v_0, then

$$N(\mathbf{r}, v, \mathbf{\Omega}, t) = \delta(v - v_0)N(\mathbf{r}, \mathbf{\Omega}, t),$$

$$f(v', \mathbf{\Omega}' \longrightarrow v, \mathbf{\Omega}) = \delta(v' - v_0)f(\mathbf{\Omega}' \longrightarrow \mathbf{\Omega}),$$

and

$$S(\mathbf{r}, v, \mathbf{\Omega}, t) = \delta(v - v_0)S(\mathbf{r}, \mathbf{\Omega}, t),$$

where $\delta(v - v_0)$ is the Dirac δ function as defined in Chapter 1, equation (14). Let $N(\mathbf{r}, \mathbf{\Omega}, t) = \int N(\mathbf{r}, v, \mathbf{\Omega}, t) \, dv$, etc. The function $N(\mathbf{r}, \mathbf{\Omega}, t)$ with the argument v missing denotes the integral of $N(\mathbf{r}, v, \mathbf{\Omega}, t)$ over the velocity v. The integral term on the right-hand side of the Boltzmann equation becomes

$$\iint v'c(v')\Sigma(v')\delta(v' - v)f(\mathbf{\Omega}' \longrightarrow \mathbf{\Omega})\delta(v' - v_0)N(\mathbf{r}, v', \mathbf{\Omega}', t) \, dv' \, d\Omega'$$

$$= \delta(v - v_0)v_0 c(v_0)\Sigma(v_0)\int N(\mathbf{r}, \mathbf{\Omega}', t)f(\mathbf{\Omega}' \longrightarrow \mathbf{\Omega}) \, d\Omega'.$$

Integrating the transport equation over v results in the following one velocity group equation

$$\frac{\partial N(\mathbf{r}, \mathbf{\Omega}, t)}{\partial t} = -v_0\mathbf{\Omega} \cdot \text{grad } N(\mathbf{r}, \mathbf{\Omega}, t) - v_0\Sigma N(\mathbf{r}, \mathbf{\Omega}, t)$$

$$+ v_0 c(v_0)\Sigma(v_0)\int N(\mathbf{r}, \mathbf{\Omega}', t)f(\mathbf{\Omega}' \longrightarrow \mathbf{\Omega}) \, d\Omega' + S(\mathbf{r}, \mathbf{\Omega}, t); \quad (2)$$

$v_0 N(\mathbf{r}, \mathbf{\Omega}, t)$ is the angular distribution of the neutron flux and will be denoted by $\psi(\mathbf{r}, \mathbf{\Omega}, t)$.

The time *independent* one velocity group equation can be obtained also under less stringent conditions. It is assumed that:

(i) there is no variation of $\Sigma(v)$ and $c(v)$ with neutron velocity;

(ii) the value of $f(\Omega' \longrightarrow \Omega) = \int f(v', \Omega' \longrightarrow v, \Omega) \, dv$ is independent of v'. Integrating (1) without the term $\dfrac{\partial N}{\partial t}$ one obtains

$$\Omega \cdot \operatorname{grad} \psi(\mathbf{r}, \Omega) + \Sigma \psi(\mathbf{r}, \Omega) = c\Sigma \int \psi(\mathbf{r}, \Omega') f(\Omega' \longrightarrow \Omega) \, d\Omega'$$
$$+ S(\mathbf{r}, \Omega), \quad (3)$$

where
$$\psi(\mathbf{r}, \Omega) = \int v N(\mathbf{r} \; v, \Omega) \, dv,$$

and
$$S(\mathbf{r}, \Omega) = \int S(\mathbf{r}, v, \Omega) \, dv.$$

A difficulty arises when the time dependent equation is considered. One obtains the following term on integration of (1) over v

$$\frac{\partial}{\partial t} \int N(\mathbf{r}, v, \Omega, t) \, dv.$$

$\int N(\mathbf{r}, v, \Omega, t) \, dv$ is the angular distribution of the density of neutrons at the point $\mathbf{r}$ at time t. It can be related to $\psi(\mathbf{r}, \Omega, t)$ only if the average velocity is known, which entails the knowledge of the spectrum of neutrons at all points in the medium.

If the spectrum of neutrons is independent of the position in the medium, i.e.

$$N(\mathbf{r}, v, \Omega, t) = g(v)N(\mathbf{r}, \Omega, t) \quad (4)$$

then a one velocity group equation can be obtained for the case where the cross-sections vary with energy, by integrating (1) over v with $N(\mathbf{r}, v, \Omega, t)$ given by (4). This is relevant to the case where the neutrons are in thermal equilibrium with the nuclei of the medium, i.e. they have a Maxwellian distribution of velocities as given in Chapter 1, equation (3).

3.2 The form of the one group equation in various co-ordinate systems

The form of the term $\Omega \cdot \operatorname{grad} N(\mathbf{r}, v, \Omega)$ depends on the co-ordinate system used. It has been derived for plane, spherical and cylindrical geometry by Weinberg and Wigner [4].

(a) Plane geometry

In plane geometry the neutron distribution depends on one spatial co-ordinate x. The angular distribution $N(\mathbf{r}, v, \mathbf{\Omega}, t)$ is symmetrical for rotations around the x axis, and the angular co-ordinate can be chosen to be μ, the cosine of the angle between $\mathbf{\Omega}$ and the x axis.

Then $\qquad\qquad \mathbf{\Omega} \cdot \text{grad}\,(\ \ ) = \mu\dfrac{\partial(\ \ )}{\partial x}.$ (5)

(b) Spherical geometry

The angular distribution in spherical geometry depends on two variables, r the distance from the origin and μ the cosine of the angle θ between the direction $\mathbf{\Omega}$ and the radius vector to the point r (see Fig. 3.1).

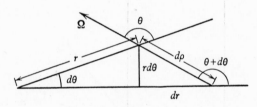

Fig. 3.1

Now $\mathbf{\Omega} \cdot \text{grad}\, N$ is the directional derivation of N along the direction $\mathbf{\Omega}$. Let ρ be the distance measured along $\mathbf{\Omega}$, but in a direction opposite to $\mathbf{\Omega}$.

Then $\qquad\qquad \mathbf{\Omega} \cdot \text{grad}\, N = -\dfrac{dN}{d\rho},$

$$= -\dfrac{\partial N}{\partial r}\dfrac{\partial r}{\partial \rho} - \dfrac{\partial N}{\partial \mu}\dfrac{\partial \mu}{\partial \rho}.$$

As $\qquad\qquad dr = -\cos\theta\, d\rho,$

$$\dfrac{dr}{d\rho} = -\cos\theta = -\mu.$$

Also $\qquad\qquad r\, d\theta = \sin\theta\, d\rho,$

$$\dfrac{d\mu}{d\rho} = -\sin\theta\dfrac{d\theta}{d\rho} = -(1-\mu^2)/r.$$

Therefore $\qquad \mathbf{\Omega} \cdot \text{grad}\, N = \mu\dfrac{\partial N}{\partial r} + \dfrac{(1-\mu^2)}{r}\dfrac{\partial N}{\partial \mu}.$ (6)

(c) Cylindrical geometry

If the system has cylindrical symmetry there will be dependence generally on two spatial co-ordinates, i.e. the distance z along the cylindrical axis and the radial distance r from the axis. Consider the case where there is no dependence on the z co-ordinate. The angular distribution $N(\mathbf{r}, v, \mathbf{\Omega}, t)$ will depend on two angular co-ordinates chosen to be θ and ω (see Fig. 3.2). θ is the angle between the z axis and the direction $\mathbf{\Omega}$ and ω is the angle between the projection of $\mathbf{\Omega}$ onto a plane perpendicular to the z axis and the radius vector in that plane. It can be seen easily that N is not independent of a rotation about a line passing through P parallel to the z axis.

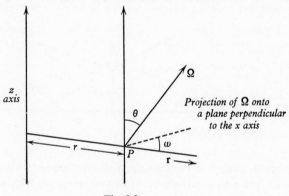

Fig. 3.2

The element of length $d\rho$ in the direction $\mathbf{\Omega}$ is given by

$$(d\rho)^2 = (dz)^2 + (r\, d\omega)^2 + (dr)^2.$$

Then
$$\frac{dN}{d\rho} = \frac{\partial N}{\partial r}\frac{\partial r}{\partial \rho} + \frac{\partial N}{\partial \omega}\frac{\partial \omega}{\partial \rho}$$

as there is no dependence on z.

Now
$$dr = \sin\theta \cos\omega\, d\rho,$$
and
$$-r\, d\omega = \sin\theta \sin\omega\, d\rho.$$

Therefore

$$\mathbf{\Omega} \cdot \operatorname{grad} N = \frac{dN}{d\rho} = \sin\theta\left(\cos\omega\, \frac{\partial N}{\partial r} - \frac{\sin\omega}{r}\frac{\partial N}{\partial \omega}\right). \qquad (7)$$

26

3.3 Solution of the transport equation in a source free medium

Consider the time independent one velocity group transport equation in plane geometry, i.e.

$$\mu \frac{\partial \psi(x, \mu)}{\partial x} + \Sigma\psi(x, \mu) = c\Sigma \int \psi(x, \mu')f(\Omega' \longrightarrow \Omega) \, d\Omega', \qquad (8)$$

where $\psi(x, \mu)$ is the angular distribution of neutron flux. It is assumed that the scattering is isotropic and that the medium is homogeneous. $f(\Omega' \longrightarrow \Omega)$ does not depend on Ω or Ω' and is equal to $\frac{1}{4\pi}$. The equation therefore reduces to

$$\mu \frac{\partial \psi(x, \mu)}{\partial x} + \Sigma\psi(x, \mu) = \tfrac{1}{2}c\Sigma \int_{-1}^{+1} \psi(x, \mu) \, d\mu. \qquad (9)$$

A solution of (9) is given by

$$\psi(x, \mu) = \exp(-\kappa x)\Theta(\mu),$$

where
$$(\Sigma - \kappa\mu)\Theta(\mu) = \tfrac{1}{2}c\Sigma \int_{-1}^{+1} \Theta(\mu) \, d\mu. \qquad (10)$$

The right-hand side of (10) is independent of μ. Hence

$$\Theta(\mu) = \frac{A}{\Sigma - \mu\kappa},$$

where A is a constant.

Substituting back into (10) one obtains the following formula for κ:

$$A = \tfrac{1}{2}c\Sigma \int_{-1}^{+1} \frac{A \, d\mu}{\Sigma - \mu\kappa},$$

$$= \frac{Ac\Sigma}{2\kappa} \ln\left[\frac{\Sigma + \kappa}{\Sigma - \kappa}\right],$$

i.e.
$$(c\Sigma/2\kappa) \ln\left[\frac{\Sigma + \kappa}{\Sigma - \kappa}\right] = \frac{c\Sigma}{\kappa} \tanh^{-1}(\kappa/\Sigma) = 1,$$

i.e.
$$\kappa/\Sigma = \tanh(\kappa/c\Sigma). \qquad (11)$$

When $c < 1$ the principal root of this equation is real; when $c > 1$ it is imaginary.

27

A solution of the homogeneous equation (9) is, therefore,

$$\psi(x, \mu) = \frac{A \exp(-\kappa x)}{\Sigma - \mu\kappa}.\ddagger \qquad (12)$$

It will be shown now that the flux $\phi(x) = 2\pi \int \psi(x, \mu) \, d\mu$ satisfies an equation

$$\frac{d^2\phi}{dx^2} = \kappa^2\phi, \qquad (13)$$

with κ given by (11). $L = \kappa^{-1}$ is called the neutron diffusion length in the medium.

In order to prove (13) the integral equation is considered. The simplified equation for the one velocity group case in plane geometry can be obtained from Chapter 2, equation (14). However, it will be instructive to obtain the equation by the integration of (9) over x. From (9)

$$2\pi \frac{\partial}{\partial x} [\exp(x\Sigma/\mu)\psi(x, \mu)] = (c\Sigma/2\mu) \exp(x\Sigma/\mu)\phi(x). \qquad (14)$$

For $\mu > 0$ equation (14) is integrated from $-\infty$ to x.
Then

$$2\pi \exp(x\Sigma/\mu)\psi(x, \mu) = (c\Sigma/2\mu)\int_{-\infty}^{x} \exp(x'\Sigma/\mu)\phi(x') \, dx'.$$

The left-hand side of this equation vanishes at the lower limit $x = -\infty$. For $\mu < 0$ equation (14) is integrated from x to ∞. Then

$$-2\pi \exp(+x\Sigma/\mu)\psi(x, \mu) = (c\Sigma/2\mu)\int_{x}^{\infty} \exp(+x'\Sigma/\mu)\phi(x') \, dx'.$$

Therefore

$$\phi(x) = 2\pi \int_{-1}^{+1} \psi(x, \mu) \, d\mu,$$

$$= \tfrac{1}{2}c\Sigma \int_{0}^{1} (1/\mu) \exp(-x\Sigma/\mu)\int_{-\infty}^{x} \exp(x'\Sigma/\mu)\phi(x') \, dx' \, d\mu$$

$$-\tfrac{1}{2}c\Sigma \int_{-1}^{0} (1/\mu) \exp(-x\Sigma/\mu)\int_{x}^{\infty} \exp(+x'\Sigma/\mu)\phi(x') \, dx' \, d\mu,$$

$$= \tfrac{1}{2}c\Sigma \int_{0}^{1} (1/\mu)\int_{-\infty}^{+\infty} \exp[-\Sigma |x - x'|/\mu]\phi(x') \, dx' \, d\mu,$$

‡ A rigorous discussion of this type of solution of the transport equation (9) has been given by Case [57].

i.e. $\phi(x) = \frac{1}{2}c\Sigma \int_{-\infty}^{+\infty} E_1(\Sigma \mid x - x' \mid)\phi(x') \, dx',$ \hfill (15)

where $E_1(t)$ is the exponential integral $\int_1^\infty v^{-1} \exp(-vt) \, dv$.

$\phi(x')$ is expanded as a Taylor series about the point x, i.e.

$$\phi(x') = \sum_{n=0}^\infty \frac{1}{(n!)} \frac{d^n\phi(x)}{dx^n} (x' - x)^n. \tag{16}$$

Substituting (16) into (15) and carrying out the elementary integrations it is found that

$$\phi(x) = c[\phi(x) + \tfrac{1}{3}\Sigma^{-2} \, d^2\phi/dx^2 + \tfrac{1}{5}\Sigma^{-4} \, d^4\phi/dx^4 \ldots].$$

If $\phi(x)$ satisfies the equation

$$d^2\phi/dx^2 = \kappa^2\phi,$$

where $\qquad 1 = c[1 + \tfrac{1}{3}\Sigma^{-2}\kappa^2 + \tfrac{1}{5}\Sigma^{-4}\kappa^4 \ldots], \hfill (17)$

i.e. $\qquad \kappa/\Sigma = \tanh(\kappa/c\Sigma),$

then $\phi(x)$ satisfies the integral equation.

In order to show that the solution of the transport equation has a form like (12) in a medium at points remote from sources and boundaries, it is necessary to solve several idealized problems.

3.4 Plane source of neutrons in an infinite medium

(a) Solution for a point source

The solution of the time independent transport equation for a plane source in an infinite medium will be considered. It is very easy to obtain the solution for a point source from that for the plane source by the following transformation.

Consider a plane source at $x = 0$ (see Fig. 3.3).

Let $\phi_{pl}(x)$ be the flux due to the plane source at $x = 0$, and $\phi_{pt}(r)$ the flux due to a point source at $r = 0$.

Then $\qquad \phi_{pl}(x) = \int_0^\infty \phi_{pt}[(r^2 + x^2)^{\frac{1}{2}}]2\pi r \, dr,$

if a source density of one neutron per unit area is assumed.

Let $\qquad u^2 = r^2 + x^2.$

Then $\qquad \phi_{pl}(x) = 2\pi \int_x^\infty \phi_{pt}(u)u \, du.$

Differentiating with respect to x the following relation is obtained

$$\phi_{pt}(x) = -\frac{1}{2\pi x}\cdot\frac{d\phi_{pl}}{dx}. \tag{18}$$

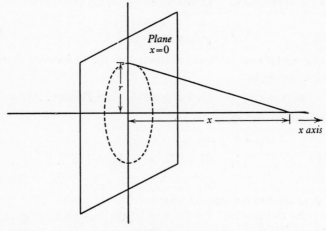

Fig. 3.3

(b) Solution of the transport equation by Fourier transform

The transport equation describing the neutron distribution from a plane source at $x = 0$ in an infinite uniform medium is

$$\mu\frac{\partial\psi(x, \mu)}{\partial x} + \Sigma\psi(x, \mu) = \tfrac{1}{2}c\Sigma\int_{-1}^{+1}\psi(x, \mu)\,d\mu + \delta(x)/4\pi. \tag{19}$$

This equation can be solved by means of the Fourier transform. Let $\Pi(\tau, \mu)$ be the Fourier transform of $\psi(x, \mu)$, i.e.,

$$\Pi(\tau, \mu) = \int_{-\infty}^{+\infty}\psi(x, \mu)\exp(-i\tau x)\,dx. \tag{20}$$

Equation (19) is multiplied by $\exp(-i\tau x)$ and integrated over x. The first term on the left-hand side of (19) gives

$$\int_{-\infty}^{+\infty}\mu\frac{\partial\psi(x, \mu)}{\partial x}\exp(-i\tau x)\,dx$$
$$= \left[\mu\psi(x, \mu)\exp(-i\tau x)\right]_{-\infty}^{+\infty} + i\tau\mu\int_{-\infty}^{+\infty}\psi(x, \mu)\exp(-i\tau x)\,dx.$$

The first term on the right-hand side of this equation vanishes, and therefore the transform of equation (19) is as follows,

$$(\Sigma + i\tau\mu)\Pi(\tau, \mu) = \tfrac{1}{2}c\Sigma\int_{-1}^{+1} \Pi(\tau, \mu)\, d\mu + \frac{1}{4\pi}. \qquad (21)$$

The right-hand side of this equation is independent of μ;

therefore
$$\Pi(\tau, \mu) = \frac{\Pi_0(\tau)}{\Sigma + i\tau\mu},$$

where $\Pi_0(\tau)$ is some function of τ.

Substituting back into the equation (21), the following expression is obtained for $\Pi_0(\tau)$.

$$\Pi_0(\tau) = \tfrac{1}{2}c\Sigma\Pi_0(\tau)\int_{-1}^{+1} \frac{d\mu}{\Sigma + i\tau\mu} + \frac{1}{4\pi},$$

$$= \tfrac{1}{2}c\Sigma\Pi_0(\tau)(1/i\tau)\ln\left(\frac{\Sigma + i\tau}{\Sigma - i\tau}\right) + \frac{1}{4\pi}.$$

Now $\dfrac{1}{2i}\ln\left(\dfrac{\Sigma + i\tau}{\Sigma - i\tau}\right) = \tan^{-1}(\tau/\Sigma)$ is real.

Therefore $\quad \Pi_0(\tau) = \left(\dfrac{1}{4\pi}\right)[1 - (c\Sigma/\tau)\tan^{-1}(\tau/\Sigma)]^{-1}.$

$\psi(x, \mu)$ is obtained from the Fourier inversion formula,

$$\psi(x, \mu) = \left(\frac{1}{2\pi}\right)\int_{-\infty}^{+\infty} \Pi(\tau, \mu)\exp(i\tau x)\, d\tau,$$

$$= \left(\frac{1}{8\pi^2}\right)\int_{-\infty}^{+\infty} \exp(i\tau x)(\Sigma + i\tau\mu)^{-1}$$
$$\left[1 - (c\Sigma/2i\tau)\ln\left\{\frac{\Sigma + i\tau}{\Sigma - i\tau}\right\}\right]^{-1} d\tau. \quad (22)$$

The total flux $\phi(x)$ is obtained by integration over μ, i.e.

$$\phi(x) = 2\pi\int_{-1}^{+1} \psi(x, \mu)\, d\mu,$$

$$= \frac{1}{4\pi}\int_{-\infty}^{+\infty} (1/i\tau)\ln\left[\frac{\Sigma + i\tau}{\Sigma - i\tau}\right]\left[1 - (c\Sigma/2i\tau)\ln\left\{\Sigma - _{\tau}\right\}\right]^{-1}$$
$$\exp(i\tau x)\, d\tau. \quad (23)$$

In order to obtain a solution for $\phi(x)$ in the form of an asymptotic part $\exp(-\kappa x)$ and a transient part, the path of integration in the complex plane is taken as shown in Fig. 3.4 for $x \geqslant 0$.

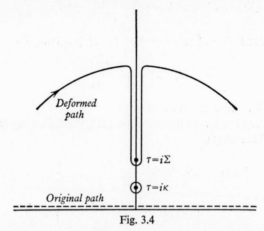

Fig. 3.4

The complex plane is cut along the imaginary axis from $i\Sigma$ to $i\infty$. The original path of integration is changed into one around the imaginary axis.

The integrand in (23) has a simple pole where the term in the denominator vanishes, i.e. where

$$c\Sigma \ln \left(\frac{\Sigma + i\tau}{\Sigma - i\tau}\right) = 2i\tau.$$

If $1 > c$ the poles are at $\tau = \pm i\kappa$, where κ is given by (11). An examination of the integrand reveals a singularity at $\tau = +i\Sigma$. This is of the form $\ln z$ for $z \longrightarrow 0$. To avoid this singularity the plane is cut and the deformed contour is taken along the imaginary axis to $i\Sigma$ and back again.

The asymptotic part of the solution is that arising from the residue at $\tau = i\kappa$, and the transient part, which is only important near to the source, arises from the contributions to the integral around the cut.

(c) Results

The contribution to the integral from the residue at $\tau = i\kappa$ is equal to

$$\frac{\kappa(\Sigma^2 - \kappa^2)\exp(-\kappa x)}{c\Sigma[\kappa^2 - \Sigma^2(1 - c)]}. \tag{24}$$

For $x < 0$ the integral (23) can be evaluated by taking a path of integration in the lower half of the complex plane. A contribution then arises from the pole $\tau = -i\kappa$, and is equal to

$$\frac{\kappa(\Sigma^2 - \kappa^2)\exp(-\kappa x)}{c\Sigma[\kappa^2 - \Sigma^2(1 - c)]}.\tag{25}$$

This part of the solution ϕ_1 can be written, therefore, in the form

$$\phi_1 = \frac{B}{2\kappa D}\exp(-\kappa|x|),\tag{26}$$

where

$$B = \frac{2(1 - c)}{c}\frac{(\Sigma^2 - \kappa^2)}{[\kappa^2 - \Sigma^2(1 - c)]},\tag{27}$$

and

$$D = \frac{(1 - c)\Sigma}{\kappa^2}.\tag{28}$$

In deriving (11) it has been assumed that $1 > c$. When fissile material is present in the system, c may be larger than unity.‡ When $c > 1$ the roots of (11) are imaginary.

Let $\kappa = i\kappa_0$, then κ_0 satisfies the equation

$$\kappa_0 = \Sigma \tan(\kappa_0/c\Sigma).\tag{29}$$

In this case the pole of the integrand in (23) occurs on the real axis.

For $x > 0$ the contribution from around the cut along the imaginary axis is the sum of the two integrals

$$I_1 = (4\pi)^{-1}\int_{i\infty}^{i\Sigma}(i\tau)^{-1}\ln\left[\frac{\Sigma + i\tau}{\Sigma - i\tau}\right]\left[1 - (c\Sigma/2i\tau)\ln\left\{\frac{\Sigma + i\tau}{\Sigma - i\tau}\right\}\right]^{-1}$$
$$\exp(i\tau x)\, d\tau,$$

where the path is on the left-hand side of the imaginary axis, and

$$I_2 = (4\pi)^{-1}\int_{i\Sigma}^{i\infty}(i\tau)^{-1}\ln\left[\frac{\Sigma + i\tau}{\Sigma - i\tau}\right]\left[1 - (c\Sigma/2i\tau)\ln\left\{\frac{\Sigma + i\tau}{\Sigma - i\tau}\right\}\right]^{-1}$$
$$\exp(i\tau x)\, d\tau,$$

where the path in this integral is on the right-hand side of the imaginary axis.

Let

$$\Sigma\eta = -i\tau - \Sigma.$$

Then $\Sigma + i\tau = -\Sigma\eta$ and $\Sigma - i\tau = 2\Sigma + \Sigma\eta$.

‡ From Chapter 2, equations (5) and (6) it can be seen that $c > 1$ if $(\nu - 1)\Sigma_f > \Sigma_c$.

In I_1
$$\ln\left[\frac{\Sigma + i\tau}{\Sigma - i\tau}\right] = -i\pi + \ln\left[\frac{\Sigma\eta}{2\Sigma + \Sigma\eta}\right],$$

and in I_2 it takes the following form:

$$i\pi + \ln\left[\frac{\Sigma\eta}{2\Sigma + \Sigma\eta}\right].$$

It can be shown that the sum of I_1 and I_2 is equal to the single integral denoted by ϕ_2, where

$$\phi_2(x) = \int_0^\infty \frac{2\Sigma^2(\eta + 1)\exp\left[-(\eta + 1)\Sigma\,|\,x\,|\,\right]d\eta}{[2\Sigma(\eta + 1) - c\Sigma\ln(2\eta^{-1} + 1)]^2 + \pi^2 c^2\Sigma^2}. \quad (30)$$

When x is small the major contribution to the integral comes from large values of η, i.e. the integral is given approximately by,

$$\int_0^\infty \frac{\exp\left(-(\eta + 1)\,|\,x\,|\,\Sigma\right)d\eta}{2(\eta + 1)} = \tfrac{1}{2}E_1(\Sigma\,|\,x\,|).$$

This is recognized as the distribution of neutrons which come directly from the source.‡

For large values of x the major contribution to the integral in (30) comes from values of η near to zero. The value of the integral decreases as $\exp(-x\Sigma)$ as $x \longrightarrow \infty$.

The solution of the transport equation can be divided, therefore, into two parts ϕ_1 and ϕ_2. ϕ_2 represents the part which is important near to the source at $x = 0$, and decreases rapidly as $\exp(-x\Sigma)$ as x tends to infinity. ϕ_1 represents the part of the solution which dominates at large values of x.

3.5 The behaviour of the solution of the transport equation near to a boundary

(a) *General discussion of the problem*

The solution of the transport equation also departs from the simple form given by (12) for points near to a boundary. The solution of equation (9) near to a boundary has been studied exhaustively in

‡ The flux of neutrons which come directly from the source is given by,
$$\frac{1}{4\pi}\int_0^\infty \frac{2\pi r\exp\left[-\Sigma(r^2 + x^2)^{\frac{1}{2}}\right]}{r^2 + x^2}\,dr = \tfrac{1}{2}\int_{|x|}^\infty \frac{\exp(-u\Sigma)}{u}\,du,$$
$$= \tfrac{1}{2}E_1(\Sigma\,|\,x\,|).$$

astrophysics. One is interested in the emergent radiation from a stellar medium where the source of radiation is deep in the medium. The angular distribution of the emergent radiation can be determined for a grey stellar atmosphere (equivalent to our one velocity case) by solving equation (9) for a half space with the source at infinity. This is called the Milne problem. In neutron transport theory the solution of the same problem determines the behaviour of the neutron flux near to the free surface of a medium.

The solution of equation (9) for a half space can be obtained by the Wiener–Hopf method [9]. This method uses analytic properties of the Fourier transforms and the solution is obtained in closed form. It will not be discussed here as it has been described in great detail by other authors [1]. Here, some properties of the solution of the transport equation will be deduced using the variational method. The same method is used in Chapter 7 to discuss the thermal neutron Milne problem.

The integral equation satisfied by the neutron flux $\phi(x)$ in the half space $x > 0$ is

$$\phi(x) = \tfrac{1}{2}\Sigma \int_0^\infty E_1(\Sigma \,|\, x - x' \,|)\phi(x') \, dx'. \tag{31}$$

It has been assumed that the medium is non-capturing, i.e. $c = 1$. This equation can be derived from (9) in the same manner that (15) was derived, using the boundary condition that $\psi(0, \mu)$ is zero for all incoming directions to the half space, i.e. for μ positive.

At points distant from the boundary $\phi(x)$ is a solution of (13). When $c = 1$, $\kappa = 0$ is the root of (11).

A solution of the transport equation which is valid at large x is given by the limit of solutions given by (12) as $\kappa \longrightarrow 0$, i.e.

$$\lim_{\kappa \to 0} \left[\frac{C_1 \exp(-\kappa x)}{\Sigma - \mu\kappa} + \frac{C_2 \exp(\kappa x)}{\Sigma + \mu\kappa} \right],$$

where C_1 and C_2 are arbitrary constants. Assuming that $C_1 + C_2$ and $\kappa(C_1 - C_2)$ are both finite as $\kappa \longrightarrow 0$, then the solution $\psi(x, \mu)$ can be written in the form

$$\left(\frac{1}{4\pi} \right)[B + Ax - l\mu A], \tag{32}$$

where A and B are arbitrary constants. l is the mean free path $(=\Sigma^{-1})$.

35

For large x the value of the flux is given by

$$\phi(x) = \tfrac{1}{2} \int_{-1}^{+1} (B + Ax - l\mu A)\, d\mu,$$

$$= Ax + B.$$

The value of A is determined by the source strength of neutrons at infinity.

The solution $\phi(x)$ of the integral equation is written as

$$\phi(x) = A[x + W(x)], \tag{33}$$

where $W(x)$ tends to a constant as x tends to infinity.

Substituting into the integral equation (31) it can be shown that $W(x)$ satisfies the equation

$$W(x) = \tfrac{1}{2}\Sigma \int_{0}^{\infty} W(x')E_1(\Sigma \,|\, x - x' \,|)\, dx' + \tfrac{1}{2}E_3(\Sigma x), \tag{34}$$

where $E_3(\Sigma x) = \displaystyle\int_{1}^{\infty} t^{-3} \exp\,(-\Sigma xt)\, dt.$

Let $\phi_{as}(x)$ denote $A[x + W(\infty)]$. The point where ϕ_{as} vanishes is called the extrapolated end point, i.e. at $x = -W(\infty)$. If the value of the extrapolated end point is known in a particular problem, then the asymptotic solution can be obtained by solving (13) with the extrapolated end point as the boundary condition. The value of $W(\infty)$ will be calculated using the variational method. Before this can be accomplished, it is necessary to carry out some algebraic manipulation.

The number of neutrons passing the plane $x = x_0$ is equal to

$$2\pi \int_{-1}^{+1} \mu\psi(x_0,\, \mu)\, d\mu. \tag{35}$$

This is called the current j at $x = x_0$. For a non-capturing medium it is constant and is equal to the number of neutrons produced per second by the source at infinity. From (32) it can be seen that

$$j = -\tfrac{1}{3}Al.$$

Let $K(x)$ be defined as follows:

$$K(x) = 2\pi \int_{-1}^{+1} \mu^2 \psi(x, \mu)\, d\mu. \tag{36}$$

From the transport equation (9) it can be seen that

$$\frac{dK(x)}{dx} = -j\Sigma,$$

i.e. $\qquad K(x) = \tfrac{1}{3}A(x + x_0)$ for all x.

From (32) $\qquad K(x) = \tfrac{1}{3}(Ax + B),$

and therefore $\qquad x_0 = B/A = W(\infty),$

where $W(x)$ is defined in (33).

By integrating equation (14), it can be shown that for $\mu < 0$

$$\psi(0, \mu) = -(\Sigma/4\pi\mu)\int_0^\infty \exp\,[x'\Sigma/\mu]\phi(x')\, dx'.$$

At $x = 0$, $\psi(x, \mu)$ is zero for all incoming directions, i.e. for $\mu > 0$. Therefore

$$K(0) = 2\pi \int_{-1}^0 \mu^2 \psi(0, \mu)\, d\mu.$$

Now $W(\infty) = 3K(0)/A$,

$$= (6\pi/A)\int_{-1}^0 \mu^2 \psi(0, \mu)\, d\mu,$$

$$= -[3\Sigma/(2A)]\int_{-1}^0 \mu \int_0^\infty \exp\,[x'\Sigma/\mu]\phi(x')\, dx'\, d\mu,$$

$$= [3\Sigma/(2A)]\int_0^\infty E_3(x'\Sigma)\phi(x')\, dx'.$$

Substituting for $\phi(x)$ from (33) then

$$W(\infty) = \tfrac{3}{8}\Sigma^{-1} + \tfrac{3}{2}\Sigma\int_0^\infty E_3(x'\Sigma)W(x')\, dx'. \tag{37}$$

In order to calculate the value of the integral on the right-hand side of (37) the functional (20) of Appendix B is used, i.e.

$$\frac{(S\phi_0)^2}{(\phi_0, L\phi_0)}.$$

For the problem at hand this is equal to

$$\frac{\frac{3}{4}\Sigma \left[\int E_3(x\Sigma)W_1(x)\,dx\right]^2}{\int_0^\infty W_1(x)[W_1(x) - \frac{1}{2}\Sigma\int_0^\infty E_1(\Sigma\,|\,x - x'\,|)W_1(x')\,dx']dx}, \quad (38)$$

where $W_1(x)$ is the trial function for $W(x)$.‡

Lecaine [10] assumed the following form for $W_1(x)$,

$$W_1(x) = 1 - A_2E_2(x\Sigma) - A_3E_3(x\Sigma), \quad (39)$$

where $E_2(x\Sigma)$ and $E_3(x\Sigma)$ are exponential integrals and A_2 and A_3 are constants to be determined by the variational method.

(38) is stationary for arbitrary variations δA_2, δA_3 in A_2 and A_3 respectively if $A_2 = 0.3428949$ and $A_3 = -0.3158704$. On substituting into (37) it is found that

$$W(\infty) = 0.7104457.$$

This value is within $4 \times 10^{-5}\%$ of the exact value obtained by the Wiener–Hopf method.

The maximum error in (39) is 0.3% for positions on the boundary, i.e. at $x = 0$, the error decreases as x increases. The emergent angular distribution $\psi(0, \mu)$ for $\mu < 0$ is given by the following expression:

$$\psi(0, \mu) = 0.501362 + 0.671543\mu + [0.2109272 + 0.194303\mu^2] \times \ln(1 + \mu^{-1}). \quad (40)$$

This has a maximum error of 0.3% at $\mu = 0$.

3.6 Milne's problem with capture

Lecaine has also considered the calculation of the extrapolation length when the half space $x > 0$ captures neutrons [11]. It has been shown that the solution of (9) by the Wiener–Hopf method gives the following expression for the asymptotic solution of the flux,

$$j(0)(\kappa/\Sigma)[2(\Sigma^2 - \kappa^2)]^{\frac{1}{2}}(1 - c)^{-\frac{1}{2}}[\kappa^2 - \Sigma^2(1 - c)]^{-\frac{1}{2}}$$
$$\sinh \kappa(x + x_0), \quad (41)$$

where κ is given by (11) and $j(0)$ is the magnitude of the current at $x = 0$, and x_0 the extrapolated end point [1]. Lecaine discusses several methods of calculation and one of these will be described here briefly.

‡ It can be shown that (38) is a maximum for the exact $W(x)$.

The neutron flux satisfies the equation

$$\phi(x) = \tfrac{1}{2}c\Sigma \int_0^\infty E_1(\Sigma \,|\, x - x' \,|)\phi(x')\,dx'. \tag{42}$$

Let

$$\phi(x) = A_1[\sinh \kappa(x + x_0) + Y(x)], \tag{43}$$

where $Y(x)$ is $0[\exp(-x\Sigma)]$. Substituting from (43) into (42) the following equation is obtained for $Y(x)$.

$$Y(x) = \tfrac{1}{2}c\Sigma \int_0^\infty E_1(\Sigma \,|\, x - x' \,|)Y(x')\,dx'$$
$$+ \tfrac{1}{2}[\cosh \kappa x_0 G_3(\kappa, x) + \sinh \kappa x_0 G_2(\kappa, x)], \tag{44}$$

where

$$G_3(\kappa, x) = \kappa c\Sigma \int_1^\infty \frac{\exp(-xt\Sigma)\,dt}{t(t^2\Sigma^2 - \kappa^2)},$$

and

$$G_2(\kappa, x) = -c\Sigma^2 \int_1^\infty \frac{\exp(-\Sigma xt)\,dt}{t^2\Sigma^2 - \kappa^2}. \tag{45}$$

By the variational technique an estimate can be made of the quantity

$$\tfrac{1}{2}\int_0^\infty [\cosh \kappa x_0 G_3(\kappa, x') + \sinh \kappa x_0 G_2(\kappa, x')]Y(x')\,dx'. \tag{46}$$

This quantity can be evaluated also directly from (44) by multiplying equation (44) by $\sinh \kappa(x + x_0)$ and integrating over the whole range of x. After some manipulation it can be shown that

$$\tfrac{1}{2}\int_0^\infty Y(x)[\cosh \kappa x_0 G_3(\kappa, x) + \sinh \kappa x_0 G_2(\kappa, x)]\,dx$$
$$= -\tfrac{1}{8}c\Sigma\kappa^{-2}[\cosh 2\kappa x_0 \ln(1 - \kappa^2\Sigma^{-2}) + \ln(1 - \kappa^2\Sigma^2)$$
$$+ 2\kappa^2(\Sigma^2 - \kappa^2)^{-1}]. \tag{47}$$

To estimate the quantity (46) by the variational method a trial function $Y_1(x) = B_3 G_3(\kappa, x) + B_2 G_2(\kappa, x)$ is taken. On substituting into a functional like (38), the value of B_2/B_3 can be obtained, which gives the extremum value of the functional. The value of the quantity (46) is obtained and can be put equal to (47), resulting in a transcendental equation for x_0.

So far the following approximation has been obtained for $\phi(x)$:

$$\phi(x) = A_1[\sinh \kappa(x + x_0) + B_3\{G_3(\kappa, x) + (B_2/B_3)G_2(\kappa, x)\}].$$

To determine the constants A_1 and B_3 some properties of $\phi(x)$ must be known. Lecaine uses (41), and also the following relation between $\phi(0)$ and $j(0)$:

$$\phi(0) = \kappa\Sigma^{-1}(1 - c)^{-\frac{1}{2}}j(0) \quad \text{(see [1])}.$$

Other trial functions are discussed which do not necessitate the above assumption.

The results of calculations using this method are listed in the following table:

TABLE 1

c	Σx_0	$c\Sigma x_0$	B_3	B_2
0·1	8·5394	0·8593	1238	1243
0·2	3·9238	0·7847	11·48	11·72
0·3	2·4947	0·7484	2·4727	2·5938
0·4	1·8249	0·7300	1·1281	1·2014
0·5	1·4408	0·7204	0·6886	0·7251
0·6	1·1923	0·7154	0·4868	0·4902
0·7	1·0181	0·7127	0·3748	0·3456
0·8	0·8891	0·7113	0·3052	0·2406
0·9	0·7896	0·7106	0·2581	0·1496
1·0	0·7104	0·7104		

The flux $\phi(x)$ is given by the expression

$$\sinh \kappa(x + x_0) + \tfrac{1}{2}c\Sigma\kappa^{-1}[(B_2 + B_3) \exp (\kappa x)E_1\{(\kappa + \Sigma)x\}$$
$$+ (B_3 - B_2) \exp (-\kappa x)E_1\{ |\Sigma - \kappa| x\} - 2B_3E_1(x\Sigma)]. \quad (48)$$

The angular distribution is related to $\phi(x)$ by

$$2\pi\psi(0, \mu) = \tfrac{1}{2}c\Sigma\mu^{-1}\int_0^\infty \phi(x') \exp (-x'\Sigma/\mu)dx'.$$

The integration results in a fairly complicated integral which will not be given.

The maximum error in the determination of x_0 is 0·3%. In the following table the variation of x_0 for values of $c > 1$ will be given. These values were calculated by Case, de Hoffmann and Placzek using the Weiner–Hopf method [12].

TABLE 2

c	$c\Sigma x_0$	c	$c\Sigma x_0$
1·0	0·7104	1·9	0·7145
1·1	0·7106	2·0	0·7151
1·2	0·7109	2·1	0·7156
1·3	0·7113	2·2	0·7162
1·4	0·7118	2·3	0·7167
1·5	0·7123	2·4	0·7172
1·6	0·7129	2·5	0·7177
1·7	0·7134	3·0	0·7199
1·8	0·7140		

The value of x_0 is given by $0·7104/(c\Sigma)$ to within 0·7% for $0·6 \leqslant c \leqslant 2$. [1].

It is convenient to define another quantity which is related to the extrapolated end point x_0. This is the extrapolation length λ and is defined as

$$\phi_{as}(0) \left/ \frac{d\phi_{as}}{dx} \right|_{x=0}, \tag{49}$$

where $\phi_{as}(x)$ is the asymptotic flux in the medium.

From (41) it can be seen that

$$\kappa\lambda = \tanh \kappa x_0.$$

When the medium is non capturing $x_0 = \lambda$. For values of c near to unity $\lambda = 0·7104c^{-\frac{1}{2}}$.

CHAPTER 4

Solution of the One Velocity Group Transport Equation by Expansion Methods

4.1 P_1 approximation

Consider the transport equation for the case of isotropic scattering. This is as follows:

$$\mathbf{\Omega} \cdot \operatorname{grad} \psi(\mathbf{r}, \mathbf{\Omega}) + \Sigma \psi(\mathbf{r}, \mathbf{\Omega}) = \frac{c\Sigma}{4\pi} \int \psi(\mathbf{r}, \mathbf{\Omega}') \, d\Omega'. \tag{1}$$

The current vector $\mathbf{j}(\mathbf{r})$ will be defined as follows:

$$\mathbf{j}(\mathbf{r}) = \int \mathbf{\Omega} \psi(\mathbf{r}, \mathbf{\Omega}) \, d\Omega, \tag{2}$$

where $\mathbf{j}(\mathbf{r})$ has the components $\int \Omega_x \psi(\mathbf{r}, \mathbf{\Omega}) \, d\Omega$, $\int \Omega_y \psi(\mathbf{r}, \mathbf{\Omega}) \, d\Omega$ and $\int \Omega_z \psi(\mathbf{r}, \mathbf{\Omega}) \, d\Omega$ in the x, y and z directions respectively. If $\psi(\mathbf{r}, \mathbf{\Omega})$ is expanded in the angular co-ordinates as a series of spherical harmonics, then the first two terms of the series can be written as follows:

$$\psi(\mathbf{r}, \mathbf{\Omega}) = (4\pi)^{-1}[\phi(\mathbf{r}) + 3\mathbf{j} \cdot \mathbf{\Omega}], \tag{3}$$

where $\phi(\mathbf{r})$ is the flux, i.e.

$$\phi(\mathbf{r}) = \int \psi(\mathbf{r}, \mathbf{\Omega}) \, d\Omega.$$

In general further terms cannot be written down in vector notation. If equation (1) is integrated over Ω with $\psi(\mathbf{r}, \mathbf{\Omega})$ given by (3) the following equation is obtained:

$$\operatorname{div} \mathbf{j} + \Sigma \phi(\mathbf{r}) = c\Sigma \phi(\mathbf{r}). \tag{4}$$

Similarly, if (1) is multiplied by $\mathbf{\Omega}$ and the equation integrated over Ω the following is obtained:

$$\tfrac{1}{3} \operatorname{grad} \phi(\mathbf{r}) + \Sigma \mathbf{j} = 0. \tag{5}$$

Substitute for **j** from (5) into (4), then

$$\nabla^2\phi(\mathbf{r}) + 3\Sigma^2(c - 1)\phi(\mathbf{r}) = 0. \tag{6}$$

This is called the P_1 approximation and is equivalent to the asymptotic equation when $c - 1$ is small. It is called the P_1 approximation because the expansion of $\psi(\mathbf{r}, \mathbf{\Omega})$ in spherical harmonics has been restricted to two terms. In the P_N approximation $(N + 1)$ terms are taken.

A brief account will be given now of various expansions which can be used to solve the transport equation. These expansion methods have been superseded by numerical methods, e.g. the Carlson method, for critical size calculations of systems which are small compared with the neutron mean free path. This is because some of the methods, e.g. the spherical harmonics method, become very complicated when the variation of cross-sections with energy is taken into account.

4.2 Spherical harmonics method

(a) Spherical harmonics method in plane geometry

The case of plane geometry will be considered in order to simplify the formulae. This will suffice to give the basic ideas of the method.

The one-velocity group transport equation for isotropic scattering and for an isotropic source constant throughout the medium is given by

$$\mu\frac{\partial\psi(x, \mu)}{\partial x} + \Sigma\psi(x, \mu) = (4\pi)^{-1}c\Sigma\phi_0(x) + S/(4\pi), \tag{7}$$

where S is the source strength and $\phi_0(x)$ is the flux. The suffix o is introduced in the symbol used to denote the flux, as ϕ_n is used to denote the coefficient of the nth term in the expansion of $\psi(x, \mu)$ in spherical harmonics. $\psi(x, \mu)$ is expanded as follows:

$$\psi(x, \mu) = (4\pi)^{-1} \sum_{n=0}^{\infty} (2n + 1)\phi_n(x)P_n(\mu), \tag{8}$$

where $$\phi_n(x) = 2\pi\int_{-1}^{+1}\psi(x, \mu)P_n(\mu)\, d\mu. \tag{9}$$

Equation (7) is multiplied by $P_n(\mu)$ and integrated over μ. Using the following relation between the $P_n(\mu)$'s:

$$(2n + 1)\mu P_n(\mu) = (n + 1)P_{n+1}(\mu) + nP_{n-1}(\mu),$$

the following set of equations is obtained:

$$(n + 1)\, \phi'_{n+1} + n\, \phi'_{n-1} = c\Sigma\phi_0\delta_{n0} - (2n + 1)\,\Sigma\phi_n + S\delta_{n0} \quad (10)$$

where $\delta_{n0} = 1$ when $n = 0$ and is zero otherwise.

A particular solution of the set of equations is

$$\phi_0 = \frac{S}{\Sigma(1 - c)} \text{ and } \phi_n = 0 \text{ for } n > 0.$$

This corresponds to a constant uniform production and absorption of neutrons. To obtain the general solution of (10) a general solution of the homogeneous equations must be added to the particular solution.

In the spherical harmonics P_N approximation, ϕ_{N+1}, ϕ_{N+2}, etc. are all put equal to zero. The equations (10) are satisfied for $n = 0, 1, 2 \ldots N$ but not for $n = N + 1$. These equations are solved by obtaining solutions which depend on x as $\exp(-x\Sigma/\beta)$.

If the last spherical harmonic retained in the expression (8) is odd (N odd), then there are $N + 1$ solutions of the form $\exp(-x\Sigma/\beta_k)$,

i.e. $$\psi_k(x, \mu) = (4\pi)^{-1}\sum_{0}^{N}(2n + 1)\phi_{k,\,n}(x)P_n(\mu),$$

where $$\phi_{k,\,n}(x) = g_n(\beta_k) \exp(-x\Sigma/\beta_k). \quad (11)$$

The general solution of Boltzmann's equation in the P_N approximation is, therefore,

$$\psi(x, \mu) = \frac{S}{4\pi\Sigma(1 - c)} + \sum_{k=0}^{N} a_k\psi_k(x, \mu), \quad (12)$$

where the a_k are arbitrary constants.

The proper choice of constants a_k ensures the continuity of the angular distribution across a boundary. In the P_N approximation the angular distribution contains only $(N + 1)$ spherical harmonics.

If $\phi_{k,\,n}(x)$ is substituted into the homogeneous part of (10) the following equations are obtained (the suffix k is dropped from β_k):

$$n = 0, \quad -g_1/\beta = (c - 1)g_0, \quad (13)$$

and for $n \geqslant 1$

$$(n + 1)g_{n+1} + ng_{n-1} - (2n + 1)\beta g_n = 0. \quad (14)$$

If the series is terminated at the Nth spherical harmonic the last equation reads

$$Ng_{N-1} = (2N + 1)g_N. \tag{15}$$

The recurrence relations (14) are satisfied by the Legendre polynomials $P_n(\beta)$ and by the polynomials $W_{n-1}(\beta)$, which are defined as follows:

$$W_{n-1}(\beta) = P_n(\beta)Q_0(\beta) - Q_n(\beta), \tag{16}$$

where $Q_n(\beta)$ are the Legendre polynomials of the second kind.

The $W_{n-1}(\beta)$ are the non-singular part of $Q_n(\beta)$.‡

The function $W_n(\beta)$, like $P_n(\beta)$ is a polynomial of degree n in β.§

It follows that the solution of (14) is given as follows:

$$g_n(\beta) = AP_n(\beta) - BW_{n-1}(\beta) \text{ for } n = 1, 2, \ldots N, \tag{17}$$

where A and B are arbitrary constants. A can be put equal to unity.

The equation (14) will be satisfied for $n = 1, 2, 3 \ldots (N - 1)$.

In order to satisfy (15) the following relation must hold:

$$N[P_{N-1}(\beta) - BW_{N-2}(\beta)] = (2N + 1)\beta[P_N(\beta) - BW_{N-1}(\beta)]$$

i.e.
$$P_{N+1}(\beta) - BW_N(\beta) = 0. \tag{18}$$

From (13)
$$g_0(\beta) = -\frac{(\beta - B)}{\beta(c - 1)},$$

and from (14) for $n = 1$,

$$g_0(\beta) = 3\beta g_1(\beta) - 2g_2(\beta) = 1.$$

This last relation follows from the formula for the g_n's, i.e. (17).

Therefore
$$B = \beta c,$$

and (18) becomes

$$P_{N+1}(\beta) = \beta c W_N(\beta). \tag{19}$$

(19) is an algebraic equation of degree $(N + 1)$ and gives $(N + 1)$ roots β_k.

‡ $Q_0(\beta) = \frac{1}{2} \ln [(1 + \beta)/(1 - \beta)]$.

§ The first $W_n(\beta)$ are as follows:

$$W_0 = 1, \; W_1 = \tfrac{3}{2}\beta, \; W_2 = \tfrac{5}{2}\beta^2 - \tfrac{2}{3}.$$

(See Jahnke and Emde [13].)

If N is odd, equation (19) has $\frac{1}{2}(N+1)$ positive roots and an equal number of negative roots. If N is even, only odd powers of β occur in (19) and one of the roots is $\beta = 0$. This complicates the formulation of the boundary conditions. Invariably it is found that any P_{2N-1} approximation is more accurate than the succeeding P_{2N} approximation. For this reason only odd order spherical harmonic approximations are considered.

The limit of (19) as $N \longrightarrow \infty$ will be considered now. For $|\beta| > 1$ the $P_{N+1}(\beta)$ and $W_N(\beta)$ can be replaced by the following expressions [13]:

$$P_{N+1}(\beta) = \frac{(2\beta)^{N+1}}{\pi^{\frac{1}{2}}(N+1)^{\frac{1}{2}}},$$

and $\quad W_N(\beta) = \dfrac{(2\beta)^{N+1} \tanh^{-1}(1/\beta)}{\pi^{\frac{1}{2}}(N+1)^{\frac{1}{2}}} - \left[\dfrac{\pi}{(N+1)(2\beta)^{2N+4}}\right]^{\frac{1}{2}}.$

Then (19) becomes

$$\beta = \tanh(1/\beta c).$$

This is identical to (11) as $\kappa = \Sigma/\beta$.

For $|\beta| < 1$ different asymptotic expansions apply and additional real roots are obtained.

The roots of (19) divide into two types, the asymptotic roots $\beta_0 \sim \kappa^{-1}$ and the transient roots which are smaller than unity.

(b) Boundary conditions

(i) In the P_N approximation there are $(N+1)$ arbitrary constants a_k. These are determined from the continuity of $\phi_n(x)$ at a boundary. The boundary conditions at infinity depend on the nature of the problem. If the medium is capturing and there is no supply of neutrons from infinity then all $\phi_n(x)$ should vanish at infinity.

(ii) The boundary conditions at a free surface will be considered now. A free surface is one on which no neutrons fall from outside so

$$\psi(0, \mu) = 0 \text{ for } \mu > 0.$$

The medium is to the right of the free surface at $x = 0$.

As $\qquad\qquad \psi(0, \mu) = 0 \text{ for } \mu > 0 \text{ then}$

$$\int_0^1 \psi(0, \mu) P_n(\mu)\, d\mu = 0. \qquad (20)$$

46

In a half space where the medium is capturing and there is no supply from infinity $\phi_n(\infty) = 0$ for all n. In order to satisfy this condition only the positive roots of (19) are considered. There are, therefore, only $\frac{1}{2}(N+1)$ arbitrary constants a_k to satisfy the boundary condition in the P_N approximation. (20) gives twice too many conditions. The odd or the even P_n's are chosen, and the odd P_n's are better for a low order approximation. These are known as the Marshak boundary conditions.

The boundary conditions can be determined in the following alternative way. The vacuum $x < 0$ is replaced by a black body (i.e. $c = 0$). At the free surface there is continuity of the $\phi_n(x)$'s.

In the fictitious medium $B = 0$ as $B = c\beta$. (19) becomes

$$P_{N+1}(\beta) = 0.$$

As $\psi(-\infty, \mu) = 0$, only the negative roots of this equation are considered.

Let the roots be $-\beta_i (i = 0, 1, \ldots \frac{1}{2}[N+1])$.

The solution for $\psi(0, \mu)$ is given, therefore, as follows:

$$\psi(0, \mu) = (4\pi)^{-1} \sum_{k=0}^{\frac{1}{2}(N+1)} a_k \sum_{n=0}^{N} (2n+1) P_n(-\beta_k) P_n(\mu). \quad (21)$$

The inner series can be summed; then

$$\psi(0, \mu) = (4\pi)^{-1}(N+1) \sum_{k=0, \beta_k > 0}^{\frac{1}{2}(N+1)} a_k(\mu + \beta_k)^{-1} P_{N+1}(\mu) P_N(-\beta_k). \quad (22)$$

(22) vanishes for all positive roots β_k of $P_{N+1}(\mu) = 0$. The boundary condition is, therefore,

$$\psi(0, \mu) = 0 \text{ for } \mu = |\beta_k|.$$

These boundary conditions are more accurate than the Marshak conditions for higher order spherical harmonics calculations, and were obtained by Mark [14].

(c) Spherical harmonics method in other geometries

The form of the operator Ω . grad $\psi(\mathbf{r}, \Omega)$ in spherical geometry is given by Chapter 3, equation (6). The transport equation in spherical geometry is, therefore

$$\mu \frac{\partial \psi(r, \mu)}{\partial r} + \frac{(1 - \mu^2)}{r} \frac{\partial \psi(r, \mu)}{\partial \mu} + \Sigma \psi(r, \mu) = \frac{c \Sigma \phi_0(r)}{4\pi} + \frac{S}{4\pi}. \quad (23)$$

If $\psi(r, \mu)$ is expanded in spherical harmonics, i.e.

$$\psi(r, \mu) = \frac{1}{4\pi} \sum_{n=0}^{\infty} (2n+1)\, \phi_n(r) P_n(\mu),$$

and (23) is multiplied by $P_n(\mu)$ and integrated over Ω, the following set of equations is obtained for the $\phi_n(r)$:

$$(n+1)[d/dr + (n+2)/r]\phi_{n+1}(r) + n[d/dr - (n-1)/r]\phi_{n-1}(r)$$
$$= c\Sigma\phi_0(r)\delta_{n0} - (2n+1)\Sigma\phi_n + S\delta_{0n}. \quad (24)$$

In order to solve the homogeneous equation a solution is sought of the form

$$\phi_{k,\,n}(r) = g_n(\beta_k) \exp{(r\Sigma/\beta_k)} \times \text{polynomial in } r^{-1}.$$

It is found that the radial function can be expressed in terms of the modified Bessel functions of the second kind [56].

$$-(-\tfrac{1}{2}\pi r)^{-\frac{1}{2}} K_{n+\frac{1}{2}}(-r).$$

In the P_N approximation a solution of the homogeneous part of equations (24) is

$$\psi_k(r, \mu) = \frac{1}{4\pi} \sum_{0}^{N} (2n+1)\phi_{k,\,n}(r) P_n(\mu),$$

$$= -\frac{1}{4\pi} \sum_{0}^{N} (2n+1)g_n(\beta_k)(-\tfrac{1}{2}\pi r\Sigma/\beta_k)^{-\frac{1}{2}} K_{n+\frac{1}{2}}(-r\Sigma/\beta_k) P_n(\mu). \quad (25)$$

The β_k and $g_n(\beta_k)$ are the same as in the plane case.

The form of $\boldsymbol{\Omega} \cdot \text{grad}\, \psi(\mathbf{r}, \boldsymbol{\Omega})$ for the case of cylindrical geometry when there is no dependence on the z co-ordinate is given by Chapter 3, equation (7). The function ψ depends on two angular co-ordinates θ and ω. $\psi(r, \theta, \omega)$ is now expanded in the associated spherical harmonics as

$$\psi(r, \theta, \omega) = \sum_{n=0}^{\infty} \sum_{m=-n}^{n} \phi_{nm}(r) P_{nm}(\Omega). \quad (26)$$

In the P_N approximation the flux $\phi_{00}(r)$ is the sum of $(N+1)$ terms of the type

$$g_{00}(\beta_k) I_0(r\Sigma/\beta_k) + g'_{00}(\beta_k) K_0(r\Sigma/\beta_k).$$

The β_k are again the solutions of (19), but the $g_{00}(\beta_k)$ and $g'_{00}(\beta_k)$ are different from the g_0 occurring in the other two geometries. For a more detailed discussion the reader should consult Davison's book [1].

4.3 Double range spherical harmonic expansion

At a plane boundary the angular distribution of neutron flux $\psi(x, \mu)$ is discontinuous at $\mu = 0$, as illustrated in Fig. 4.1.

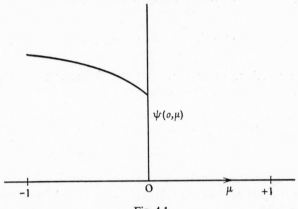

Fig. 4.1

The total flux $\phi(x)$ is non-zero at the boundary. Therefore, the flux of neutrons in a direction parallel to the plane face but just inside the medium will be non-zero. The flux of neutrons in a direction just outside the medium will be, of course, zero. At distances of the order of one mean free path from the free surface the flux variation near $\mu = 0$ is more rapid than in the rest of the range of μ.

In the spherical harmonics method the angular distribution of neutron flux is expanded in terms of functions defined over the whole range of μ. In order to describe a rapid flux variation at a particular value of μ a large number of terms in the series would be required.

A method which can be used when dealing with a discontinuity as illustrated in the figure is the double range approximation, in which different expansions are used for $\mu < 0$ and for $\mu > 0$.

The double range spherical harmonic expansion in plane geometry has been considered by Yvon [15]. The expansions replacing equation (8) are

$$\psi(x, \mu) = \frac{1}{2\pi} \sum_{n=0}^{\infty} (2n + 1)\phi_n{}^+ P_n(2\mu - 1) \text{ for } \mu > 0,$$

$$\psi(x, \mu) = \frac{1}{2\pi} \sum_{n=0}^{\infty} (2n + 1)\phi_n{}^- P_n(2\mu + 1) \text{ for } \mu < 0. \quad (27)$$

49

The $\phi_n{}^+$ are coefficients of the series for $\mu > 0$ and the $\phi_n{}^-$ are those of the series for $\mu < 0$.

Then
$$\phi_n{}^+ = 2\pi\int_0^1 P_n(2\mu - 1)\psi(x, \mu)\, d\mu,$$

and
$$\phi_n{}^- = 2\pi\int_{-1}^0 P_n(2\mu + 1)\psi(x, \mu)\, d\mu.$$

Substituting these expansions into the Boltzmann equation (7) results in the following set of equations:

$$(n + 1)\frac{d}{dx}\phi_{n+1}^{\pm}(x) + n\frac{d}{dx}\phi_{n-1}^{\pm}(x) + (2n + 1)(2\Sigma \pm d/dx)\phi_n^{\pm}(x)$$
$$= c\Sigma[\phi_0^+(x) + \phi_0^-(x)]\delta_{n0} + S\,\delta_{n0}. \quad (28)$$

The $P_N^{\pm}$ approximation is obtained by putting $\phi_{N+1}^{\pm} = 0$. The solution is again of the form (12). The β_k are roots of a determinant of order $2(2N + 1)$. Using this method it is possible to satisfy the free surface boundary condition by all $\phi_n^+(x)$ zero on the boundary.

4.4 Carlson S_n method

The range of μ can be further sub-divided and a different approximation used in each range. In the Carlson method for plane and spherical geometry the range of μ from -1 to $+1$ is divided into equal intervals and $\psi(\mu)$ taken to vary linearly with μ in each interval. The Carlson method was designed to find numerical solutions of the transport equation. It is discussed in detail in Chapter 8 when considering the energy dependent problem.

4.5 Expansion in Chebyshev polynomials

Instead of choosing an expansion in spherical harmonics $\psi(x, \mu)$ can be expanded as a series of Chebyshev polynomials $T_n(\mu)$ [16]. The expansion in terms of Chebyshev polynomials leads to a least maximum error, whereas an expansion in terms of Legendre polynomials leads to a minimum average error in the representation of $\psi(x, \mu)$. The same number of terms is assumed in both expansions.

The Chebyshev polynomials of the first kind are defined as follows:

$$T_n(\cos \theta) = \cos n\theta. \quad (29)$$

They satisfy the following orthogonality condition

$$\int_{-1}^{+1} T_m(\mu)T_n(\mu)(1 - \mu^2)^{-\frac{1}{2}} \, d\mu = 0, \, m \neq n,$$
$$\pi, \, m = n = 0,$$
$$\pi/2, \, m = n \neq 0.$$

The weight function distributes the error uniformly over the entire range of $\mu[-1, +1]$.

$\psi(x, \mu)$ is therefore expanded as follows:

$$\psi(x, \mu) = (2\pi)^{-1}\left[\pi^{-1}\phi_0(x)T_0(\mu) + \frac{2}{\pi} \sum_{n=0} \phi_n(x)T_n(\mu)\right], \tag{30}$$

where $\phi_n(x) = \int_{-1}^{+1} T_n(\mu)(1 - \mu^2)^{-\frac{1}{2}}\psi(x, \mu) \, d\mu.$

Substituting into the Boltzmann equation (7) the following set of equations is obtained:

$$\frac{d}{dx} \phi_1(x) + \Sigma(1 - c)\phi_0(x) + 2c\Sigma \sum_{n=1} (4n^2 - 1)^{-1}\phi_{2n}(x) = \tfrac{1}{2}S\pi.$$

$$\frac{d}{dx} \phi_{n+1}(x) + \frac{d}{dx} \phi_{n-1}(x) + 2\Sigma\phi_n(x) = 0 \text{ for } n > 0. \tag{31}$$

The solution of (31) is of the form

$$\phi_n(x) = \sum_k A_{n,k} \exp{(x\Sigma/\beta_k)}.$$

The $A_{n,k}$ are determined partly from the equations and partly from the boundary conditions. The β_k are roots of a determinant of order $(N + 1)$ in the Nth order approximation.

4.6 Chandrasekhar's method of discrete ordinates

This method was originally proposed by Wick [18], but the detailed development is due to Chandrasekhar [17]. A discussion of the method is strictly out of place in this section. A brief description is given, however, to show that it gives results similar to those obtained in the spherical harmonics method [19].

The source free Boltzmann equation in plane geometry for the case of isotropic scattering

$$\mu \frac{\partial \psi(x, \mu)}{\partial x} + \Sigma\psi(x, \mu) = \tfrac{1}{2}c\Sigma\int_{-1}^{+1} \psi(x, \mu) \, d\mu \tag{32}$$

is considered.

The integral on the right-hand side of this equation is replaced by the Gauss quadrature formula

$$\int_{-1}^{+1} \psi(x, \mu) \, d\mu = \sum_k H_k \psi(x, \mu_k). \tag{33}$$

The μ_k are the roots of $P_{N+1}(\mu)$ and the H_k are fixed numbers determined as follows

$$H_k = \int_{-1}^{+1} U_k(\mu) \, d\mu,$$

where
$$U_k(\mu) = \frac{P_{N+1}(\mu)}{(\mu - \mu_k)(\partial/\partial\mu)P_{N+1}(\mu)\,|_{\mu=\mu_k}}. \tag{34}$$

$U_k(\mu)$ is a polynomial of degree N vanishing at all the roots of $P_{N+1}(\mu)$ except at $\mu = \mu_k$, where it is equal to unity.

Let
$$\psi(x, \mu_k) = h_k(x). \tag{35}$$

At $\mu = \mu_k$ the Boltzmann equation becomes

$$\mu_k \frac{d}{dx} h_k(x) + \Sigma h_k(x) = \tfrac{1}{2}c\Sigma \sum_j H_j h_j(x).$$

The set of $(2N + 1)$ coupled equations are similar to the set of equations obtained in the spherical harmonics method.

In the spherical harmonics method the angular distribution in the P_N approximation is represented as a polynomial of order N

$$\psi(x, \mu) = (4\pi)^{-1} \sum_0^N (2n + 1)\phi_n(x)P_n(\mu), \tag{36}$$

$$= \sum_0^N h_n(x)U_n(\mu), \tag{37}$$

where $h_n(x)$ is given by (35).

Both (36) and (37) are polynomials of degree N equal at the points $\mu = \mu_k$.

The series (36) satisfies the following equation exactly:

$$\mu \frac{d\psi(x, \mu)}{dx} - (N + 1) \frac{d\phi_N(x)}{dx} P_{N+1}(\mu) + \Sigma\psi(x, \mu)$$
$$= \tfrac{1}{2}c\Sigma \int_{-1}^{+1} \psi(x, \mu) \, d\mu. \tag{38}$$

52

Solution of the One Velocity Group Transport Equation [4.6]

TABLE 3
Values of β_0^{-1}

c	P_1	P_3	P_5	T_1	T_3
1·0	0	0	0	0	0
0·9	0·5477	0·5256	0·5254	0·4472	0·5228
0·8	0·7746	0·7119	0·7105	0·6325	0·7028
0·7	0·9487	0·8345	0·8291	0·7746	0·8165
0·6	1·0954	0·9226	0·9096	0·8944	0·8944
0·5	1·2247	0·9888	0·9647	1·0000	0·9502
0·4	1·3416	1·0398	1·0026	1·0954	0·9914
0·3	1·4491	1·0801	1·0291	1·1832	1·0227
0·2	1·5492	1·1126	1·0480	1·2649	1·0471
0·1	1·6432	1·1392	1·0619	1·3216	1·0666
0·0	1·7321	1·1613	1·0724	1·4142	1·0824

c	T_5	$P_0^\pm$	$P_1^\pm$	$P_2^\pm$	Exact
1·0	0	0	0	0	0
0·9	0·5253	0·6324	0·5278	0·5255	0·5254
0·8	0·7097	0·8944	0·7202	0·7113	0·7104
0·7	0·8265	1·0954	0·8522	0·8322	0·8286
0·6	0·9030	1·2649	0·9518	0·9173	0·9073
0·5	0·9524	1·4142	1·0309	0·9793	0·9575
0·4	0·9840	1·5492	1·0954	1·0255	0·9856
0·3	1·0046	1·6733	1·1493	1·0607	0·9974
0·2	1·0180	1·7889	1·1948	1·0880	0·9999
0·1	1·0282	1·8974	1·2340	1·1096	1·0000
0·0	1·0353	2·0000	1·2680	1·1254	1·0000

TABLE 4
Values of the Extrapolated End Point in the Milne Problem

N	P_{2N+1}		T_{2N+1}		$P_N^\pm$
	Mark	Marshak	Mark	Marshak	
0	0·5774	0·6667	0·7071	0·7854	0·5000
1	0·6940	0·7051	0·6942	0·7129	0·7113
2	0·7039	0·7082	0·7021	—	0·7106

(38) differs from (32) by the additional term containing $(d/dx)\phi_N(x)$ as a factor.

The first two terms on the left-hand side of (38) represent a polynomial of order N and can be represented by

$$\sum_n \mu_n \frac{dh_n}{dx} U_n(\mu) \text{ as } P_{N+1}(\mu_k) = 0.$$

Hence equation (38) is equivalent to

$$\sum_n \mu_n \frac{dh_n}{dx} U_n\mu() + \Sigma \sum_n h_n(x)U_n(\mu) = \tfrac{1}{2}c\Sigma \sum_n h_n(x)H_n.$$

Putting $\mu = \mu_n$ then the Chandrasekhar equations are obtained. The angular distribution obtained in the spherical harmonics P_N approximation coincides at $\mu = \mu_k$ with the value obtained by the Chandrasekhar method.

4.7 Comparison of different expansion methods

Carter and Rowlands have compared the values of β_0^{-1} (exponent of the asymptotic solution) and the extrapolation length for the Milne problem obtained by the spherical harmonics, the double range spherical harmonics expansion and the Chebyshev expansion methods [20].

The results are illustrated in the tables on page 53.

In Table 4 the values of the extrapolated end point are to be compared with the exact value of 0·7104. The results in the table are given using both Marshak and Mark boundary conditions.

From Table 3 it can be seen that for the calculation of β_0^{-1} the P_{2N+1} approximation is better than the T_{2N+1} approximation, and the $P_N^\pm$ approximations. As regards the calculation of the extrapolated end point the double range expansion method gives better results than the full range methods. However, as regards general conclusions it seems that the P_1 approximation is usually better than any other expansion of the same order.

CHAPTER 5

Diffusion Approximation

5.1 The diffusion equation

The results which have been obtained are as follows. For a uniform scattering medium, in which the constant cross-section approximation is applicable, it has been shown for the time independent case in plane geometry that the flux $\phi(x)$ can be written as follows

$$\phi(x) = \phi_1(x) + \phi_2(x), \qquad (1)$$

where $\phi_2(x)$ is the transient solution which is important near to boundaries and near to sources. $\phi_1(x)$ is the asymptotic solution which satisfies the equation

$$\frac{d^2\phi_1(x)}{dx^2} = \kappa^2\phi_1(x), \qquad (2)$$

where κ is a solution of Chapter 3, equation (17).

The result can be generalized to other geometries. The one velocity group integral equation in any geometry is given by

$$\phi(\mathbf{r}) = \frac{c\Sigma}{4\pi} \int |\mathbf{r} - \mathbf{r}'|^{-2} \exp\left(-\Sigma\,|\mathbf{r} - \mathbf{r}'|\right)\phi(\mathbf{r}')\,dV'. \qquad (3)$$

This follows from Chapter 2, equation (14).

If $\phi(\mathbf{r})$ is expanded as a Taylor series, i.e.

$$\phi(\mathbf{r}') = \phi(x', y', z') = \phi(x, y, z) + (x' - x)\frac{\partial\phi}{\partial x} + (y' - y)\frac{\partial\phi}{\partial y} + (z' - z)\frac{\partial\phi}{\partial z} + \ldots$$

and this series substituted into (3), then it can be shown that $\phi(\mathbf{r})$ satisfies the equation

$$\phi(\mathbf{r}) = c[\phi(\mathbf{r}) + \tfrac{1}{3}\Sigma^{-2}\nabla^2\phi(\mathbf{r}) + \tfrac{1}{5}\Sigma^{-4}\nabla^4\phi(\mathbf{r}) \ldots]$$

for points $\mathbf{r}$ distant from boundaries and sources. Therefore $\phi(\mathbf{r})$ satisfies the equation

$$\nabla^2\phi(\mathbf{r}) = \kappa^2\phi(\mathbf{r}), \qquad (4)$$

E

where κ is again given by Chapter 3, equation (17). This is the solution equivalent to $\phi_1(x)$ in (1). The complete solution in any geometry can be represented, therefore, in the form

$$\phi(\mathbf{r}) = \phi_1(\mathbf{r}) + \phi_2(\mathbf{r}),$$

where $\phi_1(\mathbf{r})$ satisfies the equation (4) and $\phi_2(\mathbf{r})$ is $0[\exp(-\Sigma d)]$, where d is the distance from the nearest source or boundary. If the geometrical dimensions involved are large compared with the mean free path, then except in the neighbourhood of sources and boundaries $\phi_2(\mathbf{r})$ can be neglected in comparison with $\phi_1(\mathbf{r})$. In order to determine the solution of the diffusion equation it is necessary to specify the boundary conditions for $\phi_1(\mathbf{r})$.

The behaviour of the solution of the diffusion equation at various boundaries will now be considered, commencing with a discussion of the boundary conditions at a spherical boundary.

Consider the form of equation (3) in the case of spherical geometry, i.e. when $\phi(\mathbf{r})$ depends on one spatial coordinate r. Then (3) becomes

$$\phi(r) = \frac{c\Sigma}{4\pi} \int |\mathbf{r} - \mathbf{r}'|^{-2} \exp\left[-\Sigma |\mathbf{r}' - \mathbf{r}|\right]\phi(r') \, dV'. \tag{5}$$

Now $dV' = (r')^2 \, dr' \, d\mu \, d\omega$, where $\cos^{-1}\mu$ is the angle between $\mathbf{r}$ and $\mathbf{r}'$, and ω is the azimuthal angle around $\mathbf{r}$.

Let
$$\rho = |\mathbf{r}' - \mathbf{r}|,$$
$$= [r^2 + (r')^2 - 2rr'\mu]^{\frac{1}{2}}.$$
Then
$$\rho \, d\rho = -rr' \, d\mu.$$

(5) can be written as

$$\phi(r) = \tfrac{1}{2}c\Sigma \int_0^a \int_{|\mathbf{r}-\mathbf{r}'|}^{r+r'} \rho^{-1} r' \phi(r') \exp(-\rho\Sigma) \, d\rho \, dr', \tag{6}$$

where a is the radius of the sphere.

Then

$$r\phi(r) = \tfrac{1}{2}c\Sigma \int_0^a r'[E_1(\Sigma |r - r'|) - E_1(\Sigma |r + r'|)]\phi(r') \, dr',$$

$$= \tfrac{1}{2}c\Sigma \int_{-a}^a r' E_1(\Sigma |r - r'|)\phi(r') \, dr'. \tag{7}$$

Comparing (7) with Chapter 3, equation (15) it can be seen that (7) can be identified as the equation governing the neutron distribution in an infinite slab of thickness $2a$, and $r\phi(r)$ is the neutron flux. The boundary conditions for the asymptotic density $\phi_1(r)$ at the surface of the sphere $r = a$ are therefore

$$\phi_1(a + x_0) = 0, \tag{8}$$

and
$$a\phi_1(a) = -\lambda \frac{d[r\phi_1(r)]}{dr}\bigg|_{r=a}, \tag{9}$$

where x_0 is the extrapolated end point and λ the extrapolation distance at a slab as defined by Chapter 3, equation (49).

5.2 The boundary conditions at a free surface

The boundary condition

$$\phi_1(a + x_0) = 0 \tag{10}$$

applies for both plane and spherical geometry. It is assumed, therefore, that the extrapolated end point is the same for any shape of surface, provided that the shape is non-re-entrant. The flux ϕ_1 is assumed to vanish at a distance x_0 outside the actual surface of the medium.

The boundary condition (9) which involves the value of the flux and its normal derivative at the surface cannot be generalized easily to other geometries as it involves the curvature of the surface.

5.3 The boundary conditions at an interface

At the interface of two media there must be continuity of the normal component j_n of the current as neutrons cannot be lost on passing over the interface. Consider the number of neutrons captured in a volume V. This is equal to

$$\int_V (1 - c)\Sigma\phi_1 \, dV.$$

Now ϕ_1 satisfies the equation

$$\nabla^2\phi_1 = \kappa^2\phi_1.$$

The number captured is equal to

$$\int (1 - c)\Sigma\kappa^{-2}\nabla^2\phi_1 \, dV.$$

By Green's theorem this is equal to

$$(1 - c)\Sigma\kappa^{-2}\int_S \text{grad } \phi_1 \cdot dS, \qquad (11)$$

where S is the surface enclosing the volume V. The number captured is equal also to

$$-\int_S \mathbf{j} \cdot dS, \qquad (11a)$$

where $\mathbf{j}$ is the current. There is a negative sign outside the integral as the current is directed into the volume V. (11) and (11a) are equal for any surface S and therefore

$$\mathbf{j} = -(1 - c)\Sigma\kappa^{-2} \text{ grad } \phi_1. \qquad (12)$$

At the interface there is continuity of the normal component $\mathbf{j}_n$ of the current. Therefore, the normal component of $(1 - c)\Sigma\kappa^{-2} \text{ grad } \phi_1$ must be continuous.

It is more difficult to specify an actual boundary condition on the flux. However, Davison [1] has deduced the boundary condition for the case of a plane boundary between two media, where the flux does not vary laterally and where the values of c in the two media are not very different. The calculation was carried out using the Wiener–Hopf method and the boundary condition obtained is as follows:

$$3(1 - c)\Sigma^2\kappa^{-2}\phi_1(\mathbf{r}) \text{ is continuous.} \qquad (13)$$

When the system is very large and $(1 - c)$ is very small the boundary conditions are approximated by the continuity of $\phi_1(\mathbf{r})$ and $-\frac{1}{3}l \text{ grad } \phi_1(\mathbf{r})$. (N.B. the mean free path $l=\Sigma^{-1}$.)

In a critical size calculation of a multiplying region (i.e. $c > 1$) surrounded by a capturing reflector, there is an arbitrary constant in the expression for the flux obtained from the diffusion equation in both regions.‡

In the multiplying region the flux $\phi_1(\mathbf{r})$ satisfies an equation

$$\nabla^2\phi_1(\mathbf{r}) + \kappa_1^2\phi_1(\mathbf{r}) = 0, \qquad (14)$$

‡ The escape of neutrons from a multiplying medium is reduced when scattering material is placed around it. This scattering material, which ideally should capture as few neutrons as possible, acts as a reflector.

58

(Chapter 3, equation (11) has an imaginary root), and in the reflector satisfies an equation

$$\nabla^2 \phi_1(\mathbf{r}) = \kappa_2^2 \phi_1(\mathbf{r}).$$

The boundary condition becomes

$$\frac{3\Sigma^2(1 - c)\kappa^{-2}\phi_1(\mathbf{r})}{\Sigma(1 - c)\kappa^{-2} \operatorname{grad} \phi_1(\mathbf{r})} \text{ is continuous}$$

at the boundary between core and reflector. The same result would have been obtained if $\phi_1(\mathbf{r})$ and $l \operatorname{grad} \phi_1(\mathbf{r})$ had been assumed continuous at the boundary. However, assuming that $\mathbf{j} = -\frac{1}{3}l \operatorname{grad} \phi(\mathbf{r})$ would not ensure conservation of neutrons. The number of neutrons captured in the reflector would be different from the integrated current over the core reflector interface calculated from

$$\mathbf{j} = -\tfrac{1}{3}l \operatorname{grad} \phi(\mathbf{r}).$$

5.4 The boundary conditions at black bodies

Black bodies are those which absorb neutrons which are incident on their surface. The boundary conditions at the surface of black spheres and cylinders can be calculated as a function of their radius. If the radius is very large compared with the mean free path of the surrounding medium then the boundary conditions for a plane surface can be used. At the other end of the range the boundary conditions to be applied at a small sphere can be calculated.

(a) The boundary condition at a small black sphere

Suppose that the medium is infinite and non-capturing and has no sinks at infinity.‡ In the absence of a black body the only possible solution for the neutron flux is

$$\phi(r) = \text{constant} = \phi(\infty).$$

The angular distribution of neutron flux $\phi(r, \boldsymbol{\Omega})$ is a constant and is equal to $(4\pi)^{-1}\phi(\infty)$.

If the radius of the sphere is very small compared with the mean free path of the surrounding medium then its effect on the angular distribution will extend only a fraction of a mean free path because

---

‡ A sink is defined as a negative source. It results in the absorption of a per scribed number of neutrons per second.

the shadowing effect of the sphere will extend only over a distance of that order. On the other hand, neutrons which enter the sphere come from a distance of the order of one mean free path. The angular distribution of neutrons entering the sphere will be given approximately by $(4\pi)^{-1}\phi(\infty)$. The current of neutrons j entering the sphere at a point on its surface is given by

$$j = 2\pi \int_{-1}^{0} (4\pi)^{-1}\phi(\infty)\mu \, d\mu,$$
$$= -\tfrac{1}{4}\phi(\infty).$$

Consider a large volume V including the black body and so large that diffusion theory can be assumed to be valid near its outer surface S_2. Let S_1 denote the surface of the small black sphere.

As the medium is non-capturing

$$\nabla^2 \phi_1 = 0.$$

Using Green's theorem it follows that

$$0 = \int_V \nabla^2 \phi_1 \, dV = -\int_{S_1} \text{grad } \phi_1 \, . \, dS + \int_{S_2} \text{grad } \phi_1 \, . \, dS.$$

Therefore

$$-\tfrac{1}{3}l \int_{S_2} \text{grad } \phi_1 \, . \, dS = -\tfrac{1}{3}l \int_{S_1} \text{grad } \phi_1 \, . \, dS \qquad (15)$$

The error $\phi - \phi_1$ in the diffusion theory expression ϕ_1 is $0[\exp(-r\Sigma)]$, i.e. quite negligible for large r. The left-hand side of (15) represents the number of neutrons entering the black sphere as the region between S_1 and S_2 is non-capturing.

Therefore from (15)

$$l \text{ grad } \phi_1 \mid _{r=a} = \tfrac{3}{4}\phi(\infty), \qquad (16)$$

where a is the radius of the sphere. As $\nabla^2 \phi_1 = 0$, the solution of this equation which satisfies the boundary condition (16) is

$$\phi_1 = \phi(\infty)[1 + 0(a^2/r)].$$

At $r = a$ then

$$\frac{\phi_1}{(d\phi_1/dr)} = \tfrac{4}{3}l. \qquad (17)$$

(b) *The boundary conditions for* ϕ_1 *at black spheres and cylinders of varying radii*

The boundary conditions for ϕ_1 will be specified by the extrapolation length, and not by the extrapolated end point which becomes unrealistic when its value is greater than the radius of the black body.

It has been shown that the extrapolation length at a black sphere of vanishingly small radius is equal to $\frac{4}{3}l$. For a sphere of large radius it is equal to $0\cdot7104l$, the value at a plane boundary.

The extrapolation length λ varies monotonically with the size of the sphere. λ lies in the range $0\cdot7104$ to $\frac{4}{3}l$. The actual variation of λ/l with a/l for a black sphere and a black cylinder in a non-capturing medium has been calculated by Marshak [21], and Davison [22]. For complete details of the calculations the reader should consult Davison's book [1]. The results are shown in Fig. 5.1.

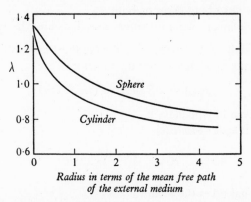

Fig. 5.1. Value of the extrapolation length λ at the surface of a black sphere and a black cylinder as a function of the radius. The unit of length is the mean free path of the external medium.

The methods employed to obtain these curves are as follows. Davison obtained the variation for small and large radii by a method of successive approximations. For example, the first approximation to the solution for large radii is that for the Milne problem. The value of λ is determined to an accuracy $0(a^{-3})$, i.e. terms of the order of a^{-3} are included, but terms of the order of $a^{-4}[\ln (a)]^4$ are omitted. For small radii λ is determined to an accuracy of $0(a^2)$ for small spheres and to an accuracy of $0(a)$ for small cylinders.

The expressions obtained by Davison do not converge in the region

61

where a is of the order of one mean free path. Marshak obtained the value of λ for intermediate values of a by the spherical harmonics method.

5.5 The boundary conditions at a grey body

A grey body is one which does not absorb all the neutrons incident on its surface.‡ The most comprehensive calculations of the extrapolation length have been made by S. Kushneriuk and C. M. McKay [23]. They calculated by the variational method the extrapolation length λ for cylinders of all radii and all degrees of greyness. They considered three cases.

(i) The cylinder is homogeneous and purely absorbing.

(ii) The cylinder consists of an inner medium which is homogeneous and purely absorbing and is surrounded by an air gap or a weakly absorbing sheet or both.

(iii) The inner medium scatters as well as absorbs neutrons.

A few details of the calculation for the third case will be given. Kushneriuk and McKay use the functional

$$J(\phi_0) = 2(S\phi_0 c\Sigma) - (\phi_0 c\Sigma, L\phi_0),$$

which is given in Appendix B.

For the integral equation

$$\phi(r) = \int c(r)\Sigma(r)k(r, r')\phi(r') \, dr' + S(r), \tag{18}$$

the functional takes the form

$$J(\phi_0) = 2\int S(r)\phi_0(r)c(r)\Sigma(r) \, dr$$
$$- \int \phi_0(r)c(r)\Sigma(r)\left\{\phi_0(r) - \int c(r')\Sigma(r')k(r,r')\phi_0(r') \, dr'\right\} dr, \tag{19}$$

where $k(r, r')$ is the kernel of the equation (18).

The flux $\phi(r)$ in the outer region is assumed to have the form $\ln(r/a) + Y(r)$. An equation for $Y(r)$ is obtained when this expression

‡ A grey body is different from a grey atmosphere as defined in astrophysics. The astrophysicists use grey to describe a medium in which the cross-sections are independent of the frequency of the radiation, i.e. it is equivalent to the one-velocity group case of neutron transport theory.

is substituted into the equation for $\phi(r)$. In the functional (19) associated with the equation defining $Y(r)$, the latter is replaced by a constant A.

It is assumed that inside the cylindrical medium that the neutron flux is given by

$$\phi(r) = BI_0(\beta r), \tag{20}$$

where β is chosen and B is determined by equating the current at infinity to the total absorption in the cylinder. The maximum value of the functional $J(\phi_0)$ is determined with respect to A. The linear extrapolation λ is given by

$$\frac{Y(a)}{(1/a) + (dY/dr)_{r=a}} = Aa. \tag{21}$$

For further details the reader should consult the original paper. In all the cases which they consider, the functional (19) is used and assumptions are made similar to those given in the calculation which

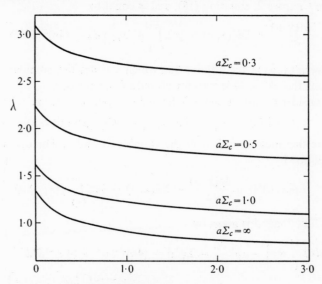

Fig. 5.2. λ for a purely absorbing cylinder

$$a\Sigma_c = \frac{\text{Radius of cylinder}}{\text{Capture mean free path in the cylinder}}$$

$a = $ Radius of the cylinder

Unit of length is equal to the mean free path in the medium surrounding the cylinder.

has been described. In Fig. 5.2 the extrapolation length at a grey non-scattering cylinder is plotted for varying degrees of greyness.

5.6 A remark on the P_1 approximation

At the beginning of Chapter 4 on the solution of the transport equation by expansion methods, equation (6) was derived. This is the equation for the flux in the P_1 approximation and is equivalent to asymptotic diffusion theory when $(1 - c)$ is small. The equations will be derived now from the transport equation using the variational method [24].

The one velocity group transport equation in plane geometry is (see Chapter 4, equation (7))

$$\mu \frac{\partial \psi(x, \mu)}{\partial x} + \Sigma \psi(x, \mu) = \tfrac{1}{2} c \Sigma \int_{-1}^{+1} \psi(x, \mu) \, d\mu + (4\pi)^{-1} S(x). \quad (22)$$

The adjoint equation can be deduced for the one-velocity group case from Chapter 2, equation (18), and is equal to

$$-\mu \frac{\partial \psi^\dagger(x, \mu)}{\partial x} + \Sigma \psi^\dagger(x, \mu) = \tfrac{1}{2} c \Sigma \int_{-1}^{+1} \psi^\dagger(x, \mu) \, d\mu + (4\pi)^{-1} S^\dagger(x), \quad (23)$$

where $\psi^\dagger(x, \mu)$ is the adjoint flux which satisfies the boundary conditions that $\psi^\dagger(x, \mu)$ is zero for all outgoing neutrons.

Consider the functional (4) defined in Appendix B, i.e.

$$J = [S^\dagger \psi(x, \mu)] + [S \psi^\dagger(x, \mu] - [\psi^\dagger(x, \mu), L\psi(x, \mu)], \quad (24)$$

where the integration is over the variables x and μ. The operator L is defined by

$$L\psi(x, \mu) = \mu \frac{\partial \psi(x, \mu)}{\partial x} + \Sigma \psi(x, \mu) - \tfrac{1}{2} c \Sigma \int_{-1}^{+1} \psi(x, \mu) \, d\mu. \quad (25)$$

The functional J is given by

$$2\pi \int dx \int_{-1}^{+1} d\mu \left[-\mu \psi^\dagger \frac{\partial \psi}{\partial x} - \Sigma \psi^\dagger \psi + (4\pi)^{-1} S \psi^\dagger + (4\pi)^{-1} S^\dagger \psi \right.$$
$$\left. + \tfrac{1}{2} c \Sigma \psi^\dagger \int_{-1}^{+1} \psi(x, \mu') \, d\mu' \right] \quad (26)$$

The following trial functions are assumed:

$$\psi(x, \mu) = (4\pi)^{-1} [\phi_0(x) + 3\mu \phi_1(x)],$$
$$\psi^\dagger(x, \mu) = (4\pi)^{-1} [\phi_0^\dagger(x) + 3\mu \phi_1^\dagger(x)]. \quad (27)$$

On integration over the variable μ the approximate value of J, say J_0, is given by

$$J_0 = (4\pi)^{-1}\int\left[S\phi_0{}^\dagger + S^\dagger\phi_0 - 3\Sigma\phi_1{}^\dagger\phi_1 - \Sigma(1-c)\phi_0\phi_0{}^\dagger \right. $$
$$\left. - \phi_1{}^\dagger\frac{d\phi_0}{dx} - \phi_0{}^\dagger\frac{d\phi_1}{dx} \right]dx. \quad (28)$$

Now the variation δJ_0 in J_0 for small variations in $\psi(x, \mu)$ and $\psi^\dagger(x, \mu)$ is given by

$$\delta J_0 = (4\pi)^{-1}\int\left[S\delta\phi_0{}^\dagger + S^\dagger\delta\phi_0 - 3\Sigma\delta\phi_1{}^\dagger\phi_1 - 3\Sigma\phi_1{}^\dagger\delta\phi_1 \right. $$
$$-\Sigma(1-c)\delta\phi_0\phi_0{}^\dagger - \Sigma(1-c)\phi_0\delta\phi_0{}^\dagger - \delta\phi_1{}^\dagger\frac{d\phi_0}{dx} - \phi_1{}^\dagger\frac{d\delta\phi_0}{dx}$$
$$\left. - \delta\phi_0{}^\dagger\frac{d\phi_1}{dx} - \phi_0{}^\dagger\frac{d\delta\phi_1}{dx} \right]dx.$$

If $\delta J_0 = 0$ for all these variations then

$$\frac{d\phi_1}{dx} + \Sigma(1-c)\phi_0 = S,$$

$$\frac{d\phi_0}{dx} + 3\Sigma\phi_1 = 0,$$

$$-\frac{d\phi_1{}^\dagger}{dx} + \Sigma(1-c)\phi_0{}^\dagger = S^\dagger,$$

$$-\frac{d\phi_0{}^\dagger}{dx} + 3\Sigma\phi_1{}^\dagger = 0. \quad (29)$$

These are the P_1 equations for isotropic scattering which are approximately the same as the asymptotic diffusion equations for $c \sim 1$. It follows that this theory is the best approximation to the one velocity transport equation when the angular distribution $\psi(x, \mu)$ is assumed to have a linear variation in μ.

5.7 The time dependent diffusion equation

The time dependent one group transport equation in plane geometry for the case of isotropic scattering is

$$\frac{1}{v}\frac{\partial\psi(x, \mu, t)}{\partial t} + \mu\frac{\partial\psi(x, \mu, t)}{\partial x} + \Sigma\psi(x, \mu, t) = \tfrac{1}{4}(c\Sigma/\pi)\phi_0(x, t)$$
$$+ \left(\frac{1}{4\pi}\right)S(x, t), \quad (30)$$

where v is the velocity of the neutrons.

65

In the P_1 approximation the first two moments $\phi_0(x, t)$ and $\phi_1(x, t)$ of the angular distribution $\psi(x, \mu, t)$ satisfy the equations

$$\frac{1}{v}\frac{\partial \phi_0(x, t)}{\partial t} + \frac{\partial \phi_1(x, t)}{\partial x} + \Sigma\phi_0(x, t) = c\Sigma\phi_0(x, t) + S(x, t), \quad (31)$$

$$\frac{1}{v}\frac{\partial \phi_1(x, t)}{\partial t} + \tfrac{1}{3}\frac{\partial \phi_0(x, t)}{\partial x} + \Sigma\phi_1(x, t) = 0. \quad (32)$$

$\phi_1(x, t)$ and its derivatives are eliminated from these equations and one obtains the following equation for $\phi_0(x, t)$:

$$\frac{\Sigma}{v}\frac{\partial \phi_0}{\partial t} + \frac{1}{v}\left[\frac{1}{v}\frac{\partial^2 \phi_0}{\partial t^2} + \Sigma(1 - c)\frac{\partial \phi_0}{\partial t}\right] = \tfrac{1}{3}\frac{\partial^2 \phi_0}{\partial x^2} + \Sigma^2(c - 1)\phi_0$$
$$+ \Sigma S + \frac{1}{v}\frac{\partial S}{\partial t}. \quad (33)$$

Generally the terms $\dfrac{1}{v^2}\dfrac{\partial^2 \phi_0}{\partial t^2}$, $\dfrac{\Sigma(1 - c)}{v}\dfrac{\partial \phi_0}{\partial t}$ and $(\Sigma v)^{-1}\dfrac{\partial S}{\partial t}$ which occur in this equation are neglected and the equation becomes

$$\frac{1}{v}\frac{\partial \phi}{\partial t} = \frac{1}{3\Sigma}\frac{\partial^2 \phi_0}{\partial x^2} - \Sigma(1 - c)\phi_0 + S. \quad (34)$$

One can neglect these terms if ϕ_0 and S vary by a small amount in an interval equal to the neutron collision time $(v\Sigma)^{-1}$, and if $c \sim 1$.

CHAPTER 6

The Neutron Spectrum during Slowing Down in an Infinite Medium

6.1 The energy spectrum in a moderator where the nuclei are at rest

After the completion of the study of the one-velocity group equation, the next subject to be considered is the calculation of the neutron spectra in a medium during slowing down.

The class of problems to be considered first is those in which it is assumed that the atomic nuclei which scatter the neutrons are initially at rest and recoil freely after a collision. In Chapter 1 it was shown that, for spherically symmetrical scattering in the centre of mass system, the probability $f(E' \longrightarrow E)$ that a neutron of energy E' is scattered into the energy range E to $E + dE$ is given as follows:

$$f(E' \longrightarrow E) = \frac{dE}{qE'} \text{ for } E' > E > (1 - q)E',$$

where
$$q = \frac{4A}{(A + 1)^2};$$

A is the atomic weight of the scattering nucleus.

Consider now the problem of a constant source in an infinite homogeneous medium. The material in the medium which slows down the neutrons is called a moderator.

Let $\phi(E)$ be the flux of neutrons at energy E. In order to obtain an equation for $\phi(E)$, the number of neutrons which enter a unit energy interval at E is equated to the number of neutrons scattered out of this energy interval per unit time, i.e.

$$\Sigma(E)\phi(E) = \int_{E}^{E(1-q)^{-1}} \Sigma_s(E')f(E' \longrightarrow E)\phi(E') \, dE' + S(E), \quad (1)$$

where $\Sigma(E)$ and $\Sigma_s(E)$ are the total and scattering macroscopic sections at energy E and $S(E)$ is the source term at energy E.

Consider the trivial case of slowing down by hydrogen for the case of no absorption, i.e. $\Sigma = \Sigma_s$ and $q = 1$. Let the source term $S(E)$ be represented by a δ function at $E = E_0$, i.e. $S \, \delta(E - E_0)$, where S is the source strength.

Equation (1) becomes

$$\Sigma(E)\phi(E) = S \, \delta(E - E_0) + \int_E^{E_0} \Sigma(E')(E')^{-1}\phi(E') \, dE'. \tag{2}$$

Let $\quad \Sigma(E)\phi(E) = A_0/E + S \, \delta(E - E_0). \tag{3}$

A solution of this form satisfies (2) if $A_0 = S$. The spectrum in an infinite medium is S/E or S on the lethargy scale.

For $q \neq 1$ the solution of equation (1) is more difficult. However, the form of the asymptotic distribution for energies removed from the energy of the neutron sources can be deduced.

Let $F(u) = E\Sigma(E)\phi(E)$, i.e. $F(u)$ is the collision density per unit lethargy. It can be verified that $F(u) = C$, where C is a constant, is a solution of (2) for energies removed from the energy of the sources. The constant C can be determined by equating the number of neutrons which pass a given lethargy value per second, i.e. $C\xi$ (ξ is the mean lethargy increase per collision) with the number of neutrons S coming from the source per second. Therefore

$$C = S/\xi,$$
$$F(u) = S/\xi, \tag{4}$$
and $\qquad \phi(E) = S/(\xi E\Sigma).$

The energy distribution of epithermal neutrons in a thermal reactor is proportional to $1/E$ to a very good approximation.

The quantity $\xi F(u)$ is called the slowing down density and the quantity $\xi\Sigma(E)$ is called the slowing down power of the moderator.

For a mixture of scattering elements (4) remains an approximate solution if $\Sigma(E)$ denotes the total scattering cross-section and ξ is replaced by an average value $\bar{\xi}$ given by

$$\bar{\xi}\Sigma(E) = \sum_i \xi_i \Sigma_i(E).$$

6.2 The transients in the collision density

The expression (4) is valid only asymptotically, that is, if the energy is not too near the source energy except in the special case of slowing down by hydrogen, where it is valid over the whole energy range.

The integral equation (2) can be solved in several ways for the case of no capture.

Marshak obtained the solution of (2) by the use of the Laplace transform. He considered the equation for $F(u)$, i.e.

$$F(u) = \delta(u) + \frac{1}{q}\int_{u-u_A}^{u} F(u') \exp\left[-(u - u')\right] du', \tag{5}$$

where $u_A = 2 \ln\left[(A + 1)/(A - 1)\right]$.

Let $Q(\eta)$ be the Laplace transform of $F(u)$, i.e.

$$Q(\eta) = \int_0^{\infty} F(u) \exp(-\eta u)\, du.$$

Multiply (5) by $\exp(-\eta u)$ and integrate over u.
Then

$$Q(\eta) = 1 + \frac{1}{q}\int_0^{\infty} \exp(-\eta u)\int_{u-u_A}^{u} F(u') \exp\left[-(u - u')\right] du'\, du,$$

$$= 1 + \frac{1}{q}\int_0^{\infty} du'\int_{u'}^{u'+u_A} F(u') \exp\left[-(u - u') - \eta(u - u') - \eta u'\right] du,$$

$$= 1 + \frac{1}{q}\int_0^{\infty} F(u') \exp(-\eta u')\, du'\int_0^{u_A} \exp\left[-y - \eta y\right] dy,$$

$$= 1 + \frac{1}{q}\, Q(\eta)X(\eta),$$

where

$$X(\eta) = \int_0^{u_A} \exp\left[-y - \eta y\right] dy,$$

$$= (1 + \eta)^{-1}[1 - \exp\{-u_A(1 + \eta)\}].$$

The Laplace inversion formula can be used to obtain $F(u)$.
The Laplace inversion formula gives

$$F(u) = \frac{1}{2\pi i}\int_{\sigma - i\infty}^{\sigma + i\infty} \frac{\exp(\eta u)\, d\eta}{1 - \dfrac{1}{q(1 - \eta)}[1 - \exp\{-u_A(1 + \eta)\}]}$$

The integration is taken over a line to the right of all the poles of the integrand which are given by

$$q(1 - \eta) = 1 - \exp[-u_A(1 + \eta)].$$

69

The only pole for which η has a non negative real part is at $\eta_0 = 0$. Writing $F(u)$ as $\delta(u)$, which is the direct source term, and a sum of residues at the poles; it can be shown that the asymptotic solution is given by $1/\xi$, i.e. the solution obtained previously.

Placzek [25] solved equation (5) by an alternative method. He considered the distribution of $\Sigma\phi_1(E)$, $\Sigma\phi_2(E)$ . . ., etc., for the neutrons which have undergone 1, 2, etc., collisions. $\Sigma\phi_1(E)$ is a discontinuous function; $\Sigma\phi_2(E)$ has a discontinuous first derivative. Let the source energy be E_0. Then

$$\Sigma(E)\phi_1(E) = S/(qE_0) \text{ for } E_0 > E > (1-q)E_0,$$
$$= 0 \text{ for } (1-q)E_0 > E.$$

$$\Sigma(E)\phi_2(E) = [S/(q^2E_0)] \ln (E_0/E) \text{ for } E_0 > E > (1-q)E_0,$$
$$= [S/(q^2E_0)] \ln [(E/E_0)(1-q)^{-2}] \text{ for } (1-q)E_0 > E$$
$$> (1-q)^2E_0,$$
$$= 0 \text{ for } (1-q)^2E_0 > E.$$

$\Sigma(E)\phi(E)$, which is equal to $\sum_i \Sigma(E)\phi_i(E)$, has a discontinuity at $(1-q)E_0$; its derivative has a discontinuity at $(1-q)^2E_0$; its second derivative has a discontinuity at $(1-q)^3E_0$, and so on.

In order to find the form of $\phi(E)$ after many collisions Placzek proceeds as follows. Only the essential steps of the analysis will be given as it would be impossible to describe all of the algebraic manipulation.

Let $\qquad x = E_0/E \quad \text{and} \quad Y(x) = E\Sigma(E)\phi(E). \qquad (6)$

Equation (1) can be written

$$Y(x) = \frac{1}{qx} \int_{(1-q)x}^{x} Y(x')\, dx' \text{ for } x > (1-q)^{-1}. \qquad (7)$$

Let $Y_n(x)$ be the solution of equation (7) for values of x in the range

$$(1-q)^{-n} \leqslant x \leqslant (1-q)^{-(n+1)}.$$

Let $\qquad z = (1/q)(1-q)^{1/q} \ln [(1-q)^n x], \qquad (8)$

i.e. $\qquad z = 0 \text{ for } x = (1-q)^{-n},$

and $\qquad z = (1-q)^{1/q} \ln [(1-q)^{-1/q}] \text{ for } x = [1-q]^{-(n+1)},$

$\qquad\qquad = \zeta.$

Let $\qquad Y_n(x) = Y_0(x)G_n(z), \qquad (9)$
where
$$Y_0(x) = q^{-1}x^{(1-q)/q}.$$

70

It can be shown by differentiating (7) with respect to x and substituting from (8) and (9) that $G_n(z)$ satisfies the equation

$$G_n(z) = G_n(0) - \int_0^z G_n(z')\, dz', \qquad (10)$$

where $\qquad G_0(z) = 1$ from (9).

A recurrent application of equation (10) gives the following:

$$G_n(z) = \sum_{m=0}^{n} G_{n-m}(0) \frac{(-z)^m}{(m!)}. \qquad (11)$$

(11) expresses $G_n(z)$ in terms of its values at the edges of the intervals. Y is a continuous function except at $x = (1-q)^{-1}$.

Therefore $\qquad G_n(0) = G_{n-1}(\zeta)$ for $n > 1$.

It can be shown that

$$G_1(0) = G_0(\zeta) - (1-q)^{1/q} = 1 - (1-q)^{1/q}. \qquad (12)$$

Let $z = \zeta$ in (11) then

$$G_{n-1}(\zeta) = G_n(0) = \sum_{m=0}^{n-1} G_{n-m-1}(0) \frac{(-\zeta)^m}{(m!)} \text{ for } n > 1. \qquad (13)$$

From (13) and (12) $G_n(0)$ is determined by iteration.

Then $\qquad G_n(0) = B_n(\zeta) - (1-q)^{1/q} B_{n-1}(\zeta),$

where $\qquad B_n(\zeta) = \sum_{m=0}^{n} (m-n) \frac{\zeta^m}{(m!)},$

and $\qquad B_0(\zeta) = 1,$

$$B_{-1}(\zeta) = 0.$$

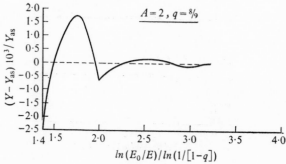

Fig. 6.1

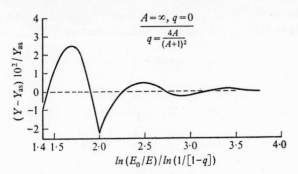

Fig. 6.2

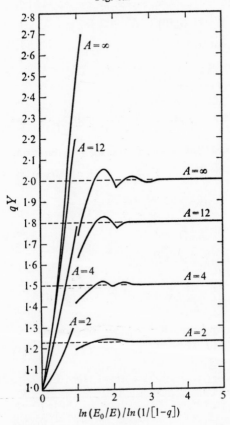

Fig. 6.3

It is possible, therefore, to determine the behaviour of $Y(x)$ for all x. After a few lethargy intervals $Y(x)$ settles down to its asymptotic value. The departure from the asymptotic form near to the source energy is illustrated in the Figs. 6.1, 6.2 and 6.3.

6.3 The slowing down of neutrons when capture is present

In the previous sections the slowing down of neutrons was considered in the absence of capture. The fraction of neutrons which escapes capture during slowing down is of great importance in the design of a thermal nuclear reactor. In the case of a reactor fuelled with natural or enriched uranium neutrons can be captured by absorption in the resonances which occur in the uranium 238 absorption cross-section. The first resonance is at 6·7 eV and about 15% of the neutrons released in fission may be absorbed in this way before they are slowed down to thermal energies, when they have a reasonable chance of absorption in the fissile material resulting in further fission. The fraction which escapes capture in this case is called the resonance escape probability. This term, however, is used sometimes in the cases where the capture cross-section does not have a resonance structure.

The spectrum of neutrons in a slowing down medium can be determined easily in the case of slowing down by hydrogen and the absorber atomic weight infinite.

(a) The energy spectrum in hydrogen

Consider the form of equation (1) for hydrogen when the source term has neutrons having very large energies, i.e. $S(E)$ extends to $S(\infty)$. The integral equation becomes

$$[\Sigma_s(E) + \Sigma_a(E)]\phi(E) = \int_E^\infty \Sigma_s(E')\phi(E') \, dE'/E' + S(E). \quad (14)$$

As the atomic weight of the absorber is assumed to be infinite it does not contribute to the slowing down. Σ_s is the macroscopic cross-section for hydrogen.

The following equation is obtained after differentiating (14) with respect to E.

$$\frac{d[\Sigma(E)\phi(E)]}{dE} = \frac{dS(E)}{dE} - \frac{\Sigma_s(E)}{\Sigma(E)} \frac{[\Sigma(E)\phi(E)]}{E}. \quad (15)$$

This equation can be solved for $\Sigma(E)\phi(E)$. After some manipulation it can be shown that

$$\Sigma(E)\phi(E) = S(E) + (1/E)\int_0^\infty S(E') \frac{\Sigma_s(E')}{\Sigma(E')}$$
$$\exp\left[-\int_E^{E'} \frac{\Sigma_a(E'')\,dE''}{\Sigma(E'')E''}\right] dE'. \quad (16)$$

When $\Sigma_a = 0$, (16) reduces to

$$\Sigma(E)\phi(E) = S + (1/E)\int_E^\infty S(E')\,dE'.$$

The presence of capture results in the collision density being attenuated first by a factor Σ_s/Σ which multiplies $S(E)$ and then by an exponential factor $\exp\left(-\int_E^{E'} \frac{\Sigma_a(E'')\,dE''}{\Sigma(E'')E''}\right)$. In a thermal reactor

$S(E) = 0$ for the region where capture takes place, say below an energy E_s. Equation (16) then becomes

$$\phi(E) = \frac{S}{E\Sigma(E)} \exp\left[-\int_E^{E_s} \frac{\Sigma_a(E')\,dE'}{\Sigma(E')E'}\right], \quad (17)$$

where
$$S = \int_{E_s}^\infty S(E')\,dE'.$$

The collision density

$$F(u) = E\Sigma(E)\phi(E),$$
$$= S \exp\left[-\int_{u_s}^u \frac{\Sigma_a(u')\,du'}{\Sigma(u')}\right],$$

where u, u_s are the lethargies corresponding to energies E and E_s. The capture during slowing down is given by

$$\int_E^{E_s} \Sigma_a(E')\phi(E')\,dE' = S\int_E^{E_s} \frac{\Sigma_a(E')}{E'\Sigma(E')} \exp\left[-\int_{E'}^{E_s} \frac{\Sigma_a(E'')\,dE''}{E''\Sigma(E'')}\right] dE',$$
$$= S\left[1 - \exp\left(-\int_E^{E_s} \frac{\Sigma_a(E')\,dE'}{E'\Sigma(E')}\right)\right].$$

The resonance escape probability during slowing down from E_s to E is given by

$$p(E_s \longrightarrow E) = 1 - (1/S)\int_E^{E_s} \Sigma_a(E')\phi(E')\, dE',$$

$$= \exp\left[-\int_E^{E_s} \frac{\Sigma_a(E')\, dE'}{E'\Sigma(E')}\right]. \tag{18}$$

If the scattering cross-section is constant then $p(E_s \longrightarrow E)$ can be written as follows

$$p(E_s \longrightarrow E) = \exp\left[-\frac{1}{\Sigma_s}\int_E^{E_s} \frac{\Sigma_a}{1 + \Sigma_A/\Sigma_s}\frac{dE'}{E'}\right].$$

The integral $\displaystyle\int_E^{E_s} \frac{\sigma_a(E')\, dE'}{(1 + \Sigma_a/\Sigma_s)E'}$, is called the effective resonance integral I_{eff}. For a dilute system Σ_s is large and the integral reduces to $\displaystyle\int_E^{E_s} \sigma_a\, dE'/E'$ which is called the resonance integral.

(b) The energy spectrum in a non-hydrogeneous medium

For any moderator the formula which is used to calculate the probability $p(E_0 \longrightarrow E)$ of survival from an energy E_0 to E is given by

$$p(E_0 \longrightarrow E) = \exp\left[-\int_E^{E_0} \frac{\Sigma_a}{\xi\Sigma}\frac{dE'}{E'}\right], \tag{19}$$

where ξ is the mean logarithmic energy loss and Σ is the total macroscopic cross-section. For hydrogen (19) goes over to (18) when $\xi = 1$.

(19) is approximate and an argument due to Weinberg and Wigner [4] will be given now in order to justify the formula.

The equation for the flux in a homogeneous absorbing moderator in an energy range in which there are no sources is

$$\Sigma(E)\phi(E) = \int_E^{E/(1-q)} \Sigma_s(E')\phi(E')\, dE'/qE'. \tag{20}$$

This equation may be rewritten as follows:

$$\Sigma(E)\phi(E) = \int_E^{E/(1-q)} \Sigma(E')\phi(E')\, dE'/(qE')$$
$$- \int_E^{E/(1-q)} \Sigma_a(E')\phi(E')\, dE'/(qE').$$

The second term on the right-hand side of this equation can be considered to represent sinks. The effect of the sinks appears below the absorption energy. The absorption at E creates a deficiency in the number of neutrons which enter the energy interval below E. The flux $\phi(E)$ of neutrons in the absorbing case can be written as

$$\phi(E) = \frac{S}{\xi E \Sigma(E)} - \int^{E_s} \frac{\Sigma_a(E')}{\Sigma(E)} Y(E'/E)\phi(E')\, dE'/E', \qquad (21)$$

where $Y(E'/E)$ is the Placzek function as defined in (6) and E_s is the energy below which the absorption takes place, and S is the source strength above E_s.

Now $Y(E'/E)$ can be written as

$$Y(E'/E) = \frac{E'}{\xi E}[1 - \varepsilon_A(u - u')], \qquad (22)$$

where u and u' are the lethargies for the energy values E and E'. The magnitude of ε_A is indicated by the curves in the Figs. 6.1, 6.2 and 6.3. Substitute for Y from (22) into (21) then

$$\xi E \Sigma(E)\phi(E) = S - \int_E^{E_s} \Sigma_a(E')[1 - \varepsilon_A(u - u')]\phi(E')\, dE',$$

$$= S - \int_E^{E_s} \Sigma_a(E')\phi(E') + \int_{-E}^{E_s} \Sigma_a(E')\varepsilon_A(u - u')\phi(E')\, dE'. \qquad (23)$$

Now the second integral on the right-hand side of (23) is small. ε_A is only appreciable over a small energy range for large A and for small A it is small anyway. The last term on the right-hand side of (23) is therefore dropped. Then

$$\xi E \Sigma(E)\phi(E) = S - \int_E^{E_s} \Sigma_a(E')\phi(E')\, dE',$$

i.e. $\qquad \xi \dfrac{d}{dE}[E\Sigma(E)\phi(E)] = [\Sigma_a(E)/E\Sigma(E)]E\Sigma(E)\phi(E). \qquad (24)$

Integrating (24) then

$$E\Sigma(E)\phi(E) = C \exp\left[-\int_E^{E_s} \frac{\Sigma_a(E')}{\xi \Sigma(E')} \frac{dE'}{E'}\right],$$

where C is an arbitrary constant. This can be determined from the condition $\xi E_s \Sigma(E_s)\phi(E_s) = S$. Therefore,

$$\xi E \Sigma(E)\phi(E) = S \exp\left[-\int_E^{E_s} \frac{\Sigma_a(E')\,dE'}{\xi\Sigma(E')E'}\right]. \tag{25}$$

The resonance escape probability is $\exp\left[-\int_E^{E_s} \frac{\Sigma_a(E')\,dE'}{\xi\Sigma(E')E'}\right]$, i.e. formula (19). The corrections to this formula are due, therefore, to the transient deviations of the actual flux in a non-absorbing medium from the asymptotic expression.

6.4 The calculation of the resonance escape probability in a reactor

A detailed discussion of this subject is strictly out of place in a book on neutron transport theory. However, an outline will be given as it provides an example of the application of the theory described in the previous sections.

(a) Homogeneous media

In order to determine the resonance escape probability in a moderating system containing uranium 238 or thorium 232, it is necessary to know the effective resonance integral I_{eff} (see 6.3 (a)), as a function of the scattering cross-section associated with each uranium or thorium atom. It can be measured directly, for example, in the case of uranium 238 by measuring the amount of 23 minute uranium 239 activity induced in a mixture of uranium 238 and scatterer placed in a $1/E$ neutron spectrum. The system is shielded with cadmium and is large enough for the correct spectrum to be obtained in the interior.

The variation of the resonance integral with temperature can also be determined experimentally. This is important as the kinetic behaviour of a reactor depends markedly on the variation of the resonance escape probability with temperature.

I_{eff} can be calculated from the resonance parameters of uranium and thorium. The task is quite a laborious one numerically. The slowing down of the neutrons as a result of collisions with the heavy nuclei cannot be ignored for all resonances, because the width of the latter is sometimes of the order of the energy loss suffered in a collision. However, the correct value of p for each resonance lies between the values obtained when either of the following assumptions is made:

(i) The width of the resonance is assumed to be infinitely small compared with the average energy loss suffered by a neutron in a collision with a heavy nucleus. This is called the narrow resonance (N.R.) approximation and in the formula (19) for p the total cross-section includes the scattering cross-section for the heavy nuclei.

(ii) The energy loss in a collision with a heavy nucleus is ignored. The total cross-section in (19) does not include the scattering cross-section of the heavy nuclei. This approximation is known as the narrow resonance infinite absorber approximation (N.R.I.A.). The N.R. approximations should be used when the width of the resonance is smaller than the energy loss, and the N.R.I.A. formula used when the reverse applies. When the energy loss is of the same order as the width, other methods can be used, for example Spinney's [26] modification of the N.R. formula.

It is possible to calculate p to an accuracy of about 1% from the basic data. The variation of p with temperature can be obtained by inserting the Doppler broadened cross-sections in formula (19).

(b) Heterogeneous media

The problem of calculation of the resonance absorption in a heterogeneous system is more difficult. For survey calculations empirical formulae are used. These formulae have a form suggested by the homogeneous medium solution, and contain arbitrary constants which are determined experimentally. Two empirical formulae will be discussed.

In the first of these formulae it is assumed that the effective resonance integral I_{eff} can be written as

$$I_{eff} = \int a(E) \, dE/E + (S/M) \int b(E) \, dE/E. \tag{27}$$

$a(E)$ and $b(E)$ are some functions of energy, S is the area of the surface of the lump and M its mass in grams. [27].

Then
$$I_{eff} = C_1 + (S/M)C_2, \tag{28}$$

where C_1 and C_2 are some constants; for uranium 238 they have values of 9·2 barns and 25 barns g/cm^2 respectively. The value of I_{eff} determined from (28) is then used in the formula for p, i.e.

$$p = \exp\left[-nI_{eff}/(\xi\Sigma_s)\right],$$

where Σ_s/n is the moderator scattering cross-section per absorber nucleus. The surface absorptions are caused by neutrons entering at resonance peaks from the moderator. The volume absorptions are due to neutrons which enter from the moderator in the regions of weaker absorption and can be degraded to energies near the resonance peaks as a result of collisions within the fuel. For larger lumps corrections must be applied for flux attenuations in the body. However, the flux attenuations are generally ignored.

The second empirical formula is suggested by a consideration of the form of the Breit-Wigner formula for the absorption cross-section. The formula is given by Chapter 1, Equation (1), i.e.

$$\frac{\frac{1}{4}\sigma_0\Gamma^2(E/E_R)^{\frac{1}{2}}}{(E - E_R)^2 + \frac{1}{4}\Gamma^2}.$$

Consider a cylindrical rod having a diameter d. The neutrons are divided into two classes; in one class the absorption mean free path is greater than d, and in the other class it is less than d. The rod is assumed to be transparent to the first class of neutrons and black to the second. The capture mean free path is less than d when the energy E lies in the interval $[E_R + \Delta E, E_R - \Delta E]$, where ΔE is given by the formula

$$C\,d = (\Delta E)^2 + \tfrac{1}{4}\Gamma^2,$$

and C is some constant. In general $\Delta E > \frac{1}{2}\Gamma$ and therefore $\Delta E/D$ varies as $d^{\frac{1}{2}}$, where D is the spacing between levels. The total absorption in the rod due to neutrons in this energy range is also proportional to the circumference of the rod, i.e. d. The other class of neutrons is supposed to be absorbed over the whole volume of the rod and is not restricted to a small part of the energy range. The total absorption is given, therefore, by an expression of the form

$$E_1\,d^2 + E_2\,d^{\frac{3}{2}} = n[H_1 + H_2(S/M)^{\frac{1}{2}}],$$

where E_1, E_2, H_1 and H_2 are constants.

This expression correlates the experimental results over a much larger range of S/M than the expression (28). It was first proposed by Gurevich and Pomeranchouk at the 1955 Geneva Conference [28].

6.5 The thermal neutron spectrum

The spectra (4) and (25) in an infinite medium were obtained with the assumption that the scattering nuclei are at rest before the collision with the neutron. In this section the assumption is not made, and the slowing down of neutrons is considered in a medium where the scattering nuclei have a Maxwell energy distribution.

The equation governing the spectrum of neutrons in the medium is

$$[\Sigma_a(E) + \Sigma_s(E)]\phi(E) = \int_0^{E_0} \Sigma_s(E')f(E' \longrightarrow E)\phi(E')\,dE' + S(E). \quad (29)$$

The limits of the integral in this equation differ from those in (1). Neutrons can now be scattered to any energy and from any energy. Strictly speaking the upper limit of the integral in (29) should be ∞, but it has been cut off at some energy E_0. The scattering cross-section satisfies the condition of detailed balance, i.e.

$$\Sigma_s(E)f(E \longrightarrow E')M(E) = \Sigma_s(E')f(E' \longrightarrow E)M(E'), \quad (30)$$

where $M(E)$ is the Maxwellian distribution for temperature T.

$$M(E) = [E/(kT)^2] \exp\left[-E/(kT)\right],$$

where k is Boltzmann's constant. To determine $f(E \longrightarrow E')$ the chemical binding of the moderating nuclei has to be taken into account. $f(E \longrightarrow E')$ is calculated easily for a monatomic gaseous moderator with a Maxwellian distribution of atomic velocities. The energy range over which these effects are important is from zero to a few electron volts.

Now
$$\Sigma_s(E)\phi(E) = \Sigma_s(E)\phi(E)\int f(E \longrightarrow E')\,dE'.$$

From (30)

$$\Sigma_s(E)\phi(E) = \phi(E)\int [M(E')/M(E)]f(E' \longrightarrow E)\Sigma_s(E')\,dE'.$$

Equation (29) can be written, therefore, as

$$\Sigma_a(E)\phi(E) = \int_0^{E_0} \left[-\frac{\phi(E)}{M(E)} + \frac{\phi(E')}{M(E')}\right]$$
$$M(E')f(E' \longrightarrow E)\Sigma_s(E')\,dE' + S(E). \quad (31)$$

Consider the energy range in which $S(E)$ is zero. It can be seen from (31) that $\phi(E) = M(E)$ is a solution when $\Sigma_a = 0$. In general it is found that the spectrum is quite insensitive to the thermal energy transfer properties of the moderator. The spectrum depends on $\gamma(E) = \Sigma_a(E)/\xi\Sigma_s$ and on the moderator temperature. For finite $\gamma(E)$ the neutrons are not able to get into complete equilibrium with the scattering nuclei; however, the thermal distribution can be characterized approximately by a neutron temperature which exceeds the moderator temperature by an amount proportional to $\gamma(E)$.

Wigner and Wilkins [29] first calculated $\Sigma_s(E)f(E \longrightarrow E')$ for a monatomic gas. They obtained the following results:

For $E' > E$,

$$f(E \longrightarrow E')(2E/\nu_1^2) = \exp[y^2 - (y')^2]\{\mathrm{erf}(\nu_1 y - \nu_2 y') + \mathrm{erf}(\nu_1 y + \nu_2 y')\} + \mathrm{erf}(\nu_1 y' - \nu_2 y) - \mathrm{erf}(\nu_2 y + \nu_1 y');$$

For $E > E'$,

$$(E \longrightarrow E')(2E/\nu_1^2) = \mathrm{erf}(\nu_1 y' - \nu_2 y) + \mathrm{erf}(\nu_1 y' + \nu_2 y) + \exp[y^2 - (y')^2]\{\mathrm{erf}(\nu_1 y - \nu_2 y') - \mathrm{erf}(\nu_2 y' + \nu_1 y)\},$$

where $E = kTy$,[2] $E' = kT(y')^2$, $\nu_1 = \frac{1}{2}(A+1)A^{-\frac{1}{2}}$, $\nu_2 = \frac{1}{2}(A-1)A^{-\frac{1}{2}}$

and
$$\mathrm{erf}(y) = \frac{2}{\pi^{\frac{1}{2}}}\int_0^y \exp(-t^2)\,dt.$$

The above formulae are for a monatomic gas. In practical moderators chemical binding effects are important. However, a considerable amount of experimental information is becoming available on the function $f(E' \longrightarrow E)$ for various moderators. This information, together with theory, has been used to derive scattering kernels for the moderators in question.

Equation (29) can be rewritten as

$$[\Sigma_a(E) + \Sigma_s(E)]\phi(E) = \int_0^{E_m} f(E' \longrightarrow E)\Sigma_s(E')\phi(E')\,dE' + S(E), \quad (32)$$

where the energy E_m is chosen to be sufficiently large, such that the probability of energy gain scattering to energies greater than E_m is negligible. The source term $S(E)$ can be written as

as
$$S(E) = \int_{E_m}^{\infty} \Sigma(E')f(E' \longrightarrow E)\,\phi_0(E')\,dE', \quad (33)$$

81

where $\phi_0(E')$ is the solution for $E' > E_m$. In a thermal reactor $\phi_0(E')$ would be represented accurately by a E^{-1} variation.

Equation (32) can be converted to a differential equation in the case of monatomic hydrogen gas [30]. In general it has to be solved numerically. An iterative procedure for the numerical solution of (32) is as follows:

A trial solution $\phi^0(E)$ to equation (32) is estimated. This solution is then re-normalized to give a function $\bar{\phi}_0(E)$ which must satisfy the following conservation condition

$$\int_0^{E_m} S(E)\, dE = \int_0^{E_m} \Sigma_a(E)\phi(E)\, dE. \qquad (34)$$

This equation is obtained from (32) by integrating over the energy range $[0, E_m]$.

Then
$$\bar{\phi}^0(E) = \frac{\phi^0(E)\displaystyle\int_0^{E_m} S(E)\, dE}{\displaystyle\int_0^{E_m} \Sigma_a(E)\phi^0(E)\, dE}.$$

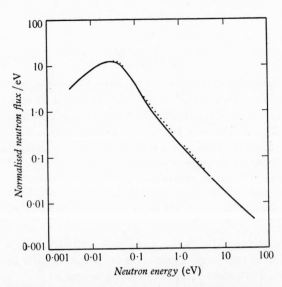

Fig. 6.4. Thermal neutron spectrum in boric acid. Temperature of the solution 291°K. Capture cross-section is 4·66 barns per hydrogen atom at 1/40ev. The full curve is the theoretical one and the points denote experimental values.

This is then substituted into the right-hand side of (32) giving

$$[\Sigma_a(E) + \Sigma_s(E)]\phi^1(E) = S(E) + \int_0^{E_m} \Sigma_s(E')f(E' \longrightarrow E)\bar{\phi}^0(E)\, dE.$$

The iterative procedure is then repeated with $\phi^1(E)$. In the numerical procedure the integral is replaced by a sum and a set of linear algebraic equations is obtained by a suitable choice of energy values.

In Fig. 6.4 the neutron spectrum in a moderator is plotted as a function Δ for a $E^{-\frac{1}{2}}$ absorption cross-section,

where
$$\Delta = \Sigma_a(kT)/(\xi\Sigma_s).$$

CHAPTER 7

Neutron Slowing Down Problems with Spatial Dependence

7.1 The thermal neutron Milne problem

In general an exact solution of the energy dependent transport equation can only be obtained numerically. The solution of the transport equation using numerical methods is discussed in Chapter 8. In the present chapter some special problems are considered, the solution of which provides insight into the general behaviour of neutrons in a slowing down medium.

(a) Transport equation

Let $\Psi(x, E \mu)$ be the flux of neutrons at a position x, having an energy E and travelling in a direction which makes an angle $\cos^{-1} \mu$ with the x axis. The half space for $x > 0$ contains non-capturing moderating material with an isotropic transfer cross-section $\Sigma(E \longrightarrow E')$. $[\Sigma(E \longrightarrow E') = \Sigma_s(E)f(E \longrightarrow E')$, where $f(E \longrightarrow E')$ is defined in Chapter 6].

The transport equation for this problem has the form

$$\mu \frac{\partial \Psi}{\partial x} + \Sigma(E)\Psi = \frac{1}{2}\int_0^\infty dE' \int_{-1}^{+1} \Sigma(E' \longrightarrow E)\Psi(x, E', \mu')\, d\mu', \quad (1)$$

subject to the boundary condition that

$$\Psi(0, E, \mu) = 0 \text{ for } 1 > \mu > 0. \tag{2}$$

The energy transfer cross-section obeys the condition of detailed balance, i.e.

$$\Sigma(E' \longrightarrow E)M(E') = \Sigma(E \longrightarrow E')\, M(E), \tag{3}$$

where the Maxwellian distribution $M(E)$ is given by

$$E(kT)^{-2} \exp{(-E/kT)}.$$

The source of neutrons is assumed to be in thermal equilibrium with the moderator at infinity in the half space $x > 0$.

When the mean free path is constant the neutron spectrum will be Maxwellian throughout the medium, because

$$\Psi(x, E, \mu) = \psi(x, \mu)M(E)$$

is a solution of equation (1), where $\psi(x, \mu)$ satisfies the one group equation

$$\mu \frac{\partial \psi(x, \mu)}{\partial x} + \Sigma\psi(x, \mu) = \tfrac{1}{2}\Sigma \int_{-1}^{+1} \psi(x, \mu') \, d\mu'. \tag{4}$$

This can be verified easily by substitution into (1) using the detailed balance condition (3).

If $\Sigma(E)$ is not constant then the function $\Psi(x, E, \mu)$ is not separable in space and energy. Equation (1) can be rewritten as

$$\mu \frac{\partial \Psi}{\partial x} + \Sigma(E)\Psi = \tfrac{1}{2}\Sigma(E)\int_{-1}^{+1}\Psi(x, E, \mu) \, d\mu + \tfrac{1}{2}S(x, E), \tag{5}$$

where

$$S(x, E) = \int_{0}^{\infty}\Sigma(E' \longrightarrow E)\int_{-1}^{+1}\Psi(x, E' \, \mu) \, d\mu \, dE'$$
$$- \int_{0}^{\infty}\Sigma(E \longrightarrow E')\int_{-1}^{+1}\Psi(x, E, \mu) \, d\mu \, dE'.$$

Because of different leakage rates from the surface caused by the variations in the mean free path with energy, a source of non-thermal neutrons $S(x, E)$ is set up near to the boundary. [$S(x, E)$ is zero when the cross-section is independent of energy.] The neutrons from $S(x, E)$ must diffuse a certain distance L_1 into the medium before attaining thermal equilibrium. Since in a heavy moderator many collisions are required to bring about thermal equilibrium, L_1 may be many times the maximum mean free path l. This is the significant difference between the mono-energetic Milne problem and the energy dependent case. In the former case deviations from the asymptotic distribution occur only over a distance one mean free path from the boundary. In the present case the deviations occur over a much larger distance.

(b) The extrapolation distance

The theory which will be described now is due to Schofield [31]. It differs in some points of detail from the original analysis due to

Nelkin [32]. Schofield's analysis should lead to more accurate values of the extrapolation distance.

Consider the solution of equation (1) for large distances into the medium. It can be seen in analogy with the solution of the one velocity group equation (see Chapter 3, equation (32)) that for large x

$$\Psi(x, E, \mu) = \left(\frac{1}{4\pi}\right)[x + x_0(E) - \mu l(E)]M(E), \tag{6}$$

provided that $x_0(E)$ satisfies the equation

$$\int \Sigma(E \longrightarrow E')[x_0(E') - x_0(E)] \, dE' = 0. \tag{7}$$

$l(E)$ is the mean free path at energy E, i.e. $l(E) = [\Sigma(E)]^{-1}$. This can be seen by substituting from (6) into (1) and using the condition of detailed balance (3). For a practical moderator where $\Sigma(E \longrightarrow E')$ is a reasonably behaved function, the solution of equation (7) is that $x_0(E)$ equals a constant. However, in certain special cases, e.g. when $\Sigma(E \longrightarrow E')$ is a Dirac δ function, $x_0(E)$ can be a function of energy. When $x_0(E)$ is independent of energy it is the linear extrapolation length appropriate to the energy dependent Milne problem.

Let $j(x)$ be the current, i.e.

$$j(x) = 2\pi \int_0^\infty \int_{-1}^{+1} \mu\Psi(x, E, \mu) \, d\mu \, dE.$$

The current is negative as the source is at infinity and the neutrons are migrating towards the boundary $x = 0$.

Integrate equation (1) over μ then

$$\frac{\partial j}{\partial x} = 0,$$

i.e. j is equal to a constant. From (6)

$$j = -\tfrac{1}{3}\bar{l},$$

where
$$\bar{l} = \int_0^\infty l(E)M(E) \, dE.$$

Multiply (1) by $l\mu$ and integrate over angle and energy. Then

$$\frac{\partial K}{\partial x} = -j,$$

86

where
$$K(x) = 2\pi \int_0^\infty l(E) \int_{-1}^{+1} \mu^2 \Psi(x, E, \mu) \, d\mu \, dE. \tag{10}$$

Therefore $K = \frac{1}{3}\bar{l}(x + x_0)$, where x_0 is the average linear extrapolation length. The function $K(x)$ is analogous to that considered in the one velocity group case (see Chapter 3, equation (32)).

From (6) the following expression is obtained for x_0:

$$x_0 \bar{l} = \int_0^\infty x_0(E) l(E) M(E) \, dE, \tag{11}$$

and from (10)

$$x_0 \bar{l} = 6\pi \int_0^\infty l(E) \int_{-1}^0 \mu^2 \Psi(0, E, \mu) \, d\mu. \tag{12}$$

(11) is rather a trivial relation when $x_0(E)$ is constant for a practical moderator.

Let $\quad \Psi(x, E, \mu) = M(E)\Psi_1(x, E, \mu) \tag{13}$

and $\quad \Psi_1(x, E, \mu) = \left(\frac{1}{4\pi}\right)[x + x_0(E) - \mu l(E)] + \Psi_2(x, E, \mu). \tag{14}$

Then the source term $S(x, E)$ of equation (5) is given as follows:

$$S(x, E) = 2\pi \int_0^\infty \Sigma(E' \longrightarrow E) \int_{-1}^{+1} \Psi(x, E', \mu) \, d\mu \, dE'$$

$$- 2\pi \int_0^\infty \Sigma(E' \longrightarrow E) \int_{-1}^{+1} \Psi(x, E, \mu) \, d\mu \, dE'.$$

Using (3) and (13) it can be shown that

$$S(x, E) = M(E)S_1(x, E),$$

where $\quad S_1(x, E) = \int_0^\infty \Sigma(E \longrightarrow E')[\Phi_1(x, E') - \Phi_1(x, E)] \, dE', \tag{15}$

and $\quad \Phi_1(x, E) = 2\pi \int_{-1}^{+1} \Psi_1(x, E, \mu) \, d\mu. \tag{16}$

Let $\quad \Phi_2(x, E) = 2\pi \int_{-1}^{+1} \Psi_2(x, E, \mu) \, d\mu. \tag{17}$

Then $\quad S_1(x, E) = \int_0^\infty \Sigma(E \longrightarrow E')[\Phi_2(x, E') - \Phi_2(x, E)] \, dE'. \tag{18}$

G

87

The solution of the mono-energetic Milne problem will also be used in the analysis. The solution of the equation (4)

$$\left[\mu \frac{\partial}{\partial x} + \Sigma\right]\psi(x, \mu, l) = \tfrac{1}{2}\Sigma\phi(x, l)$$

was shown in Chapter 3, Section 3.5, to have an asymptotic form

$$x + 0.7104l.$$

Let the Green's function for a plane isotropic source in the infinite medium be denoted by $\phi_1(x' \longrightarrow x, l)$. $\phi_1(x' \longrightarrow x, l)$ is the flux at x due to a plane isotropic source at the point x' emitting one neutron/cm²/sec. The form of $\phi(x' \longrightarrow x, l)$ is required for large x. This can be obtained using the optical reciprocity theorem which is described in Appendix C. The following result can be obtained from the optical reciprocity theorem:

$$\phi_1(x' \longrightarrow \infty, l) = \phi_1(\infty \longrightarrow x', l). \tag{19}$$

Now $\phi(\infty \longrightarrow x', l)$ is $(3/l)\phi(x, l)$, where $\phi(x, l)$ is the flux in the Milne problem. (The factor $3/l$ arises from the fact that the current in the Milne problem is $\tfrac{1}{3}l$.)

Substitute from (13) into (1) gives the following equation for $\Psi_1(x, E, \mu)$:

$$\left[\mu \frac{\partial}{\partial x} + \Sigma(E)\right]\Psi_1(x, E, \mu) = \left(\frac{1}{4\pi}\right)\Sigma(E)\Phi_1(x, E) + \left(\frac{1}{4\pi}\right)S_1(x, E) \tag{20}$$

(c) *Two special cases*

(i) if $l(E)$ is independent of energy, equation (1) is separable in space and energy, i.e.

$$\Psi(x, E, \mu) = M(E)\psi(x, \mu). \tag{21}$$

The extrapolation distance $x_0 = 0.7104l$.

(ii) If there is no coupling between different energies

$$\Sigma(E \longrightarrow E') = \Sigma(E)\delta(E - E').$$

Then $\qquad\qquad \Psi(x, E, \mu) = M(E)\psi[x, \mu, l(E)], \tag{22}$

and $\qquad\qquad\qquad x_0(E) = 0.7104l(E).$

From (11) $\qquad\qquad\qquad x_0 = 0.7104\overline{l^2}/\overline{l}. \tag{23}$

Therefore, in general

$$\bar{l}x_0 = 0{\cdot}7104\overline{l^2} - 3z_0. \tag{24}$$

z_0 tends to zero as the rate of thermalization tends to zero (case ii), and as the deviations from constant mean free path tend towards zero (case i).

(d) Variational principle for the extrapolation distance

Schofield chooses an approach which gives the correct approach in limiting cases (i) and (ii) of 7·1 (c).

Equation (20) without the source term $\left(\dfrac{1}{4\pi}\right) S_1(x, E)$ is the equation for the Milne problem for neutrons of energy E. Then the solution of (20) can be written in terms of $S_1(x, E)$ as follows:

$$\Phi_1(x, E) = \phi[x, l(E)] + \int_0^\infty \phi_1[x' \longrightarrow x, l(E)] S_1(x', E)\, dx', \tag{25}$$

where $\Phi_1(x, E)$ is given by (16) and $\phi[x, l(E)]$ is the flux in the Milne problem.

For $x \longrightarrow \infty$ equation (25) becomes

$$x_0(E) = 0{\cdot}7104 l(E) + \frac{3}{l(E)} \int_0^\infty \phi[x', l(E)] S_1(x', E)\, dx', \tag{26}$$

where use has been made of relation (19). Multiply equation (26) by $M(E)l(E)$ and integrate over E. Then

$$x_0\bar{l} = 0{\cdot}7104\overline{l^2} + 3\int_0^\infty M(E)\int_0^\infty \phi[x', l(E)] S_1(x', E)\, dx'\, dE. \tag{27}$$

Comparing (24) and (27) it can be seen that

$$z_0 = -\int_0^\infty M(E)\int_0^\infty \phi[x', l(E)] S_1(x', E)\, dx'\, dE. \tag{28}$$

z_0 is estimated by the variational method.

Consider the form of the functional (19) of Appendix B in the present case. It becomes

$$z_0[\Phi_2(x, E)] = -\int_0^\infty M(E)\, dE \int_0^\infty S_1(x, E)\, \times$$

$$\left[2\phi\{x, l(E)\} - \Phi_1(x, E) + \int_0^\infty \phi_1\{x' \longrightarrow x, l(E)\} S_1(x', E)\, dx' \right] dx. \tag{29}$$

(29) reduces to (28) for the exact $\Phi_1(x, E)$ which satisfies (25). The relation between Φ_1 and Φ_2 can be found by the integration of (14) over Ω, i.e.

$$\Phi_1(x, E, \mu) = x + x_0(E) + \Phi_2(x, E, \mu)$$

$S_1(x, E)$ is given by (18).

It can be shown that

$$\int_0^\infty M(E) \int_0^\infty S_1(x, E) A(x) \, dx \, dE = 0,$$

where $A(x)$ is an energy independent function of x. This follows because $\int_0^\infty M(E) S_1(x, E) \, dE$ is equal to div $\mathbf{j}$, where $\mathbf{j}$ is the total current which is constant, i.e. div $\mathbf{j} = 0$.

Unfortunately no detailed calculations have been made yet using the functional (29).

(e) Nelkin's calculation [**32**]

Let
$$\Phi(x, E) = 2\pi \int_{-1}^{+1} \Psi(x, E, \mu) \, d\mu \tag{30}$$

$$= xM(E) + Y(x, E), \tag{31}$$

where $\quad Y(x, E) = [x_0(E) + \Phi_2(x, E)] M(E).$

$\Phi_2(x, E)$ is the function used in Schofield's analysis.

The extrapolation length is given by formula (12), i.e.

$$x_0 \bar{l} = 6\pi \int_0^\infty l(E) \int_{-1}^0 \mu^2 \Psi(0, E, \mu) \, d\mu, \, dE. \tag{32}$$

Now for $\mu < 0$

$$\Psi(0, E, \mu) = \left(\frac{1}{4\pi}\right) \int_0^\infty \exp\left[x/\{\mu l(E)\}\right] dx/\mu \int_0^\infty \Phi(x, E') \times \\ \Sigma(E' \longrightarrow E) \, dE'. \tag{33}$$

Substitute from (31) for $\Phi(x, E)$ and use relation (3), then

$$\Psi(0, E, \mu) = \frac{\mu}{4\pi} l(E) M(E) \\ + \frac{1}{4\pi\mu} \int_0^\infty \exp\left[\frac{x}{\mu l(E)}\right] dx \int_0^\infty Y(x, E') \Sigma(E' \longrightarrow E) \, dE'. \tag{34}$$

Therefore

$$2\pi \int_{-1}^{0} \mu^2 \Psi(0, E, \mu)\, d\mu = \tfrac{1}{8} l(E) M(E)$$
$$+ \tfrac{1}{2} \int_{0}^{\infty} E_3[x/l(E)] \int_{0}^{\infty} Y(x, E') \Sigma(E' \longrightarrow E)\, dE'\, dx, \quad (35)$$

where
$$E_n(x) = \int_{1}^{\infty} \exp{(-xt)} t^{-n}\, dt.$$

Substituting into (32)

$$x_0 \bar{l} = \tfrac{3}{8} \overline{l^2(E)}$$
$$+ \tfrac{3}{2} \int_{0}^{\infty} \int_{0}^{\infty} \int_{0}^{\infty} l(E) E_3[x/l(E)] \Sigma(E' \longrightarrow E) Y(x, E')\, dE\, dE'\, dx. \quad (36)$$

$Y(x, E)$ satisfies the integral equation

$$Y(x, E) = \tfrac{1}{2} l(E) M(E) E_3[x/l(E)]$$
$$+ \tfrac{1}{2} \int_{0}^{\infty} \int_{0}^{\infty} E_1[\,|x - x'|/l(E)] \Sigma(E' \longrightarrow E) Y(x', E')\, dE'\, dx'. \quad (37)$$

The functional (20) of Appendix B is used. Therefore, the value of the integral on the right-hand side of (36) is given by

$$\dfrac{\tfrac{3}{2}\left[\displaystyle\int_{0}^{\infty}\int_{0}^{\infty}\int_{0}^{\infty} l(E) E_3[x/l(E)] \Sigma(E' \longrightarrow E) Y_1(x, E')\, dE\, dE'\, dx\right]^2}{2\displaystyle\int_{0}^{\infty}\int_{0}^{\infty}\int_{0}^{\infty} Y_1(x, E) \Sigma(E' \longrightarrow E)[M(E)]^{-1}}$$
$$\left[Y_1(x, E') - \tfrac{1}{2}\int_{0}^{\infty}\int_{0}^{\infty} E_1[\,|x - x'|/l(E')] \times \right.$$
$$\left. \Sigma(E'' \longrightarrow E') Y_1(x', E'')\, dE''\, dx'\right] dE\, dE'\, dx, \quad (38)$$

where $Y_1(x, E)$ is the trial function. The simplest trial function is the asymptotic solution $Y_1(x, E) = CM(E)$, where C is a constant. The value of x_0 for this case is given by

$$x_0 = \tfrac{3}{8} \frac{\overline{l^2}}{\bar{l}} + \tfrac{1}{3} \bar{l}.$$

For the case of constant mean free path this reduces to $0.7083l$, which is 0.3% smaller than the exact value. Nelkin also calculates the extrapolation distance in water where the cross-section has a $E^{-\frac{1}{2}}$ variation. He assumed that the anisotropic scattering in the water can be taken into account by replacing the mean free path by the transport mean free path. He obtains an extrapolation distance for water which is 7% greater than that obtained from the diffusion coefficient and the assumption of constant cross-sections. All these calculations do not take account, however, of the departure from an equilibrium velocity distribution near the boundary. Kladnik and Kuščer [33] have used Nelkin's method in estimating the spectrum for a monatomic gas moderator.

It is obvious that a considerable amount of numerical work will be carried out using these methods during the next few years.

7.2 The age equation

(a) The derivation of the age equation from the transport equation

This equation describes approximately the diffusion and thermalization of fast neutrons in a medium due to elastic collisions with the nuclei. In deriving this equation the angular distribution is expanded in a series of spherical harmonics and the expansion cut off after the first two terms, i.e. a P_1 approximation is considered. Then approximations are made regarding the variation of various quantities with energy. The derivation has been considered by many authors [1, 4, 8].

The transport equation satisfied by the collision density for the case of plane geometry will be considered. Let $F(x, u, \mu)$ be the angular distribution of the collision density. The collision density as a function of the lethargy was considered in Chapter 6, Section 6.1, where F was defined as follows

$$F(x, u, \mu) = E\Sigma(E)\Psi(x, E, \mu). \tag{39}$$

Ψ was defined in Section 7.1. The reason for considering the collision density as a function of lethargy is as follows. It has been shown previously, Chapter 6, Section 6.1, that in an infinite uniform non-capturing medium the asymptotic collision density as a function of lethargy is constant. In the derivation of the age equation the collision density is expanded as a Taylor series in the lethargy, and it can be expected that this series converges fairly rapidly.

Alternatively, the collision density could be expanded as a Taylor series in the powers of the energy, but this expansion could not be expected to converge as rapidly as an expansion in the lethargy.

For the case of elastic collisions the Boltzmann equation is as follows:

$$\mu l(u) \, \partial F / \partial x + F$$
$$= 2\pi \int_{u-u_A}^{u} c(u') \int_{-1}^{+1} F(x, u', \mu') f(\mu_0, u - u') \, d\mu' \, du'$$
$$+ \text{ source terms}, \quad (40)$$

where u_A is the maximum lethargy change in a collision, $c(u)$ is the mean number of secondaries per collision, $l(u)$ is the neutron mean free path as a function of the lethargy, μ_0 is the cosine of the angle between the direction of the neutron before and after collision, and $f(\mu_0, u - u')$ is the probability that a neutron of lethargy u' is scattered through an angle $\cos^{-1} \mu_0$, resulting in a lethargy change $(u - u')$.

Chapter 1, equation (16) gives the probability for scattering from a velocity v' to a velocity in the interval v to $v + dv$.

The lethargy $u = \ln (E_0/E)$, where E_0 is some arbitrary chosen energy and E is the neutron energy, i.e. $u = 2 \ln (v_0/v)$. Replacing the velocities v and v' by the lethargies u and u' then it can be shown that

$$f(\mu_0, u - u') \, du \, d\Omega_0$$
$$= \frac{(A + 1)^2}{8\pi A} \exp \left[-(u - u') \right] \delta[\mu_0 - \tfrac{1}{2}(A + 1) \exp \{ -\tfrac{1}{2}(u - u') \}$$
$$+ \tfrac{1}{2}(A - 1) \exp \{ \tfrac{1}{2}(u - u') \}] du \, d\Omega_0. \quad (41)$$

The function f is expanded in a series of Legendre polynomials, i.e.

$$f(\mu_0, u - u') = \frac{1}{4\pi} [f_0(u - u') + 3\mu_0 f_1(u - u') \ldots]. \quad (42)$$

It is easily verified that

$$f_0(u) = (1/q) \exp (-u) \quad (43)$$

and $f_1(u) = (1/2q)[(A + 1) \exp (-3u/2) - (A - 1) \exp (-u/2)]$,

where $q = 4A/(A + 1)^2$ is defined in Chapter 1.

The function F is also expanded in a series of spherical harmonics, i.e. $F(x, u, \mu) = (4\pi)^{-1}[F_0(x, u) + 3\mu F_1(x, u) \ldots]. \quad (44)$

In the P_1 approximation the moments $F_0(x, u)$ and $F_1(x, u)$ satisfy the following equations:

$$l(u) \, \partial F_1(x, u)/\partial x + F_0(x, u) = \int_{u-u_A}^{u} c(u') f_0(u - u') F_0(x, u') \, du', \quad (45)$$

$$\tfrac{1}{3} l(u) \, \partial F_0(x, u)/\partial x + F_1(x, u) = \int_{u-u_A}^{u} c(u') f_1(u - u') F_1(x, u') \, du'. \quad (46)$$

$F_0(x, u')$ is expanded as a Taylor series in u', i.e.

$$c(u')F_0(x, u') = [1 - \Sigma_a(u')/\Sigma(u')][F_0(x, u) \\ + (u' - u) \, \partial F_0(x, u)/\partial u \ldots]. \quad (47)$$

If the capture cross-section $\Sigma_a(u')$ is small

$$c(u')F_0(x, u') = F_0(x, u) + (u' - u) \, \partial F_0(x, u)/\partial u \\ - [\Sigma_a(u')/\Sigma(u')]F_0(x, u). \quad (48)$$

Substitute from (48) into the right-hand side of (45), which then becomes

$$F_0(x, u)\int_{u-u_A}^{u} f_0(u - u') \, du' + \partial F_0(x, u)/\partial u \int_{u-u_A}^{u} (u' - u)f_0(u - u') \, du' \\ - F_0(x, u)\int_{u-u_A}^{u} [\Sigma_a(u')/\Sigma(u')]f_0(u - u') \, du'.$$

Now
$$\int_{u-u_A}^{u} f_0(u - u') \, du' = \int_{0}^{u_A} f_0(w) \, dw = 1,$$

and

$$\int_{u-u_A}^{u} (u' - u)f_0(u - u') \, du' = - \int_{0}^{u_A} wf_0(w) \, dw = - \, \xi,$$

where ξ is the mean logarithmic energy loss. Let

$$\int_{u-u_A}^{u} \left[\frac{\Sigma_a(u')}{\Sigma(u')}\right] f_0(u - u') \, du'$$

be denoted by $[\Sigma_a/\Sigma]_{av}$.

Equation (45) becomes

$$l(u) \, \partial F_1(x, u)/\partial x = -\xi \, \partial F_0(x, u)/\partial u - [\Sigma_a/\Sigma]_{av}F_0(x, \mu). \quad (49)$$

All the terms of this equation are much smaller than the $F_0(x, u)$ term which was cancelled by the first approximation to the integral. Small differences between F_0 and the first approximation entail inaccuracy of (49).

All the terms of equation (46) are of the same order of magnitude. The integral on the right-hand side of (46) can be replaced, therefore, by

$$c(u)F_1(x, u)\int_{u-u_A}^{u} f_1(u - u')\, du'.$$

Now $\quad \int_{u-u_A}^{u} f_1(u - u')\, du' = \iint \mu_0 f(\mu_0, w)\, dw\, d\Omega',$

$$= [\cos \theta]_{av} = b,$$

where b is the average of the cosine of the angle of scatter.

(46) becomes

$$F_1(x, u)[1 - c(u)b(u)] = -\tfrac{1}{3}l(u)\ \partial F_0(x, u)/\partial x. \qquad (50)$$

Substitute for $F_1(x, u)$ from (50) into (49). The following equation is obtained for F_0:

$$\partial(\xi F_0)/\partial u = [l^2(u)/3(1 - bc)]\partial^2 F_0/\partial x^2 - [\Sigma_a/\Sigma]_{av}F_0. \qquad (51)$$

If sources are present then there is a term $S(u)$ on the right-hand side of (51). Let

$$F_0(x, u) = \chi(x, u)\exp\left[-(1/\xi)\int_0^u [\Sigma_a/\Sigma]_{av}\, du\right]. \qquad (52)$$

The following equation is obtained for $\chi(x, u)$ after substituting for F_0 from (52) into (51).

$$\partial(\xi\chi)/\partial u = \tfrac{1}{3}[l^2(u)/(1 - bc)]\ \partial^2\chi/\partial x^2. \qquad (53)$$

Let $\qquad\qquad \tau = \tfrac{1}{3}\int_0^u l^2(u)/(1 - bc)\, du, \qquad (54)$

i.e. $\qquad\qquad \dfrac{d\tau}{du} = \tfrac{1}{3}l^2(u)/(1 - bc).$

Therefore $\qquad\qquad \partial\chi/\partial\tau = \partial^2\chi/\partial x^2. \qquad (55)$

(55) is called the age equation and τ is called the Fermi age.

(b) A physical derivation of the age equation

Since the average change in the lethargy u of a neutron per collision ξ is independent of the lethargy, it follows that a time plot of u of a neutron from the fission energy down to thermal lethargy will take the form shown in Fig. 7.1.

It consists of a series of steps of approximately equal height ξ, but of gradually increasing length due to the fact that the neutron travels at a lower speed between collisions. The plot of u against t varies from one neutron to another. If the medium consists of nuclei of

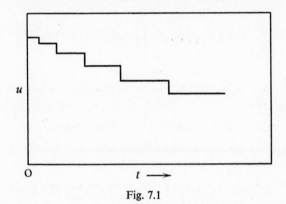

Fig. 7.1

moderate or high mass the spread of neutron energies is relatively small and as a result the histogram can be replaced by a smooth curve. It will be assumed that all the neutrons which have diffused for a time t after leaving their source have the same lethargy u.

The number of collisions which a neutron undergoes in a time dt is $\Sigma_s v \, dt$, where Σ_s is the macroscopic scattering cross-section. In the time dt the neutron lethargy will have changed by an amount du,

where
$$du = \xi \Sigma_s v \, dt. \tag{56}$$

Consider a volume element dV at x and the neutrons which have diffused for a time t. The leakage of neutrons of velocity v from a volume element dV at x at time t is

$$\operatorname{div} \mathbf{j} \, dV.$$

In the P_1 approximation

$$\mathbf{j} = -\tfrac{1}{3}[vl(v)/(1 - bc)] \, \partial N_0(x, t)/\partial x.$$

The number of neutrons captured in the elementary volume dV is

$$v \Sigma_a N_0(x, t).$$

96

Then

$$\partial N_0(x, t)/\partial t = -\text{div } \mathbf{j} - v\Sigma_a N_0(x, t),$$
$$= [\tfrac{1}{3}vl(v)/(1 - bc)] \, \partial^2 N_0(x, t)/\partial x^2 - v\Sigma_a N_0(x, t). \quad (57)$$

Let $N_0(x, u)$ be the number of neutrons per cm^3 with lethargy between u and $u + du$. Then on the continuous slowing down model

$$N_0(x, t) \, dt = N_0(x, u) \, du,$$

i.e.
$$N_0(x, t) = N_0(x, u)(du/dt),$$
$$= \xi v\Sigma_s N_0(x, u) \text{ from (56).} \quad (58)$$

Now
$$\partial N_0(x, t)/\partial t = \partial u/\partial t \; \partial N_0(x, t)/\partial u,$$
$$= \xi v\Sigma_s \; \partial N_0(x, t)/\partial u,$$
$$= \xi v\Sigma_s \; \partial/\partial u[\xi v\Sigma_s N_0(x, u)].$$

From (57)

$$\tfrac{1}{3}[vl(v)/(1 - bc)]\partial^2/\partial x^2[\xi v\Sigma_s N_0(x, u)]$$
$$= \xi v\Sigma_s \partial/\partial u[\xi v\Sigma_s N_0(x, u)]$$
$$+ v\Sigma_a[\xi v\Sigma_s N_0(x, u)]. \quad (59)$$

Let
$$\xi v\Sigma_s N_0(x, u) = \chi(x, u) \exp\left[-\int_0^u du\Sigma_a/(\xi\Sigma_s)\right]$$

and
$$\tau = \tfrac{1}{3}\int_0^u \frac{l^2(u') \, du'}{\xi c(1 - bc)}.$$

Then
$$\partial^2\chi/\partial x^2 = \partial\chi/\partial\tau. \quad (60)$$

This is the same as equation (55). The formula for τ is the same as (54) for the case where the capture is small, i.e. $c \sim 1$. Equation (60) has been derived on the assumption that at a given time after emission from the source the neutron has a definite lethargy u.

For a plane source in an infinite medium the solution of equation (55) is

$$\chi(x, \tau) = (4\pi\tau)^{-\frac{1}{2}} \exp[-x^2/4\tau]. \quad (61)$$

Now
$$\frac{\displaystyle\int_0^\infty x^2\chi(x, \tau) \, dx}{\displaystyle\int_0^\infty \chi(x, \tau) \, dx} = 2\tau, \quad (61)$$

i.e. τ is one half of the mean square distance travelled by a neutron in slowing down to lethargy u; $\tau^{\frac{1}{2}}$ is called the slowing down length.

(c) *The range of applicability of age theory*

In the derivation of the age equation from the Boltzmann equation it is assumed that:

(i) The chance of capture is small.

(ii) The distribution is nearly isotropic.

(iii) The energy change in one collision is small and within the interval of the energy change all the functions $F(x, u)$, $c(u)$ and $l(u)$ can be expressed as Taylor series.

From the assumption that the distribution is almost isotropic, a condition can be obtained on the range over which age theory is valid. The assumption $F_0 \gg F_1$ means that

$$F_0 \gg -\tfrac{1}{3}[l(u)/(1-b)] \; \partial F_0(x, u)/\partial x. \tag{62}$$

Substituting for F_0 the solution for a plane source in an infinite medium, i.e. $C \exp[-x^2/4\tau]$, where C is some constant, then the following condition is obtained:

$$3(1-b)2\tau \gg xl(u),$$

i.e.
$$L_s^2 \gg xl(u). \tag{63}$$

This is a necessary condition. It will be shown that (63) is not sufficient and that a stricter condition is necessary to determine the range x over which the age theory expression is valid, as a function of lethargy from the energy of the source.

Consider the diagrammatic representation (Fig. 7.2). To bridge the gap the age equation is solved as though applicable up to the source energy E_0.

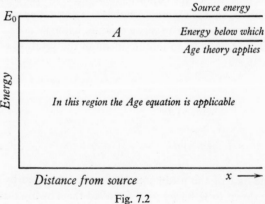

Fig. 7.2

The following criterion can be used to decide whether or not the correct solution has been obtained. Consider the neutrons which have been scattered once. In the region where the age equation is a valid approximation, the same answer should be obtained with either the original or the iterated source distribution.

The solution for a plane source in an infinite medium is

$$(4\pi\tau)^{-\frac{1}{2}} \exp[-x^2/4\tau]. \tag{64}$$

The position of the sources of neutrons which have undergone one collision is given by

$$\tfrac{1}{2}[l(u_0)]^{-1}E_1[\,|x|\,/l(u_0)], \tag{65}$$

where u_0 is the source lethargy.

The expression for χ when the source distribution is given by (65) is as follows:

$$\chi = (4\pi\tau)^{-\frac{1}{2}}\int_{-\infty}^{+\infty} E_1[\,|x'|\,/l(u_0)]\exp[-(x-x')^2/4L_s^2]\,dx'/2l(u_0). \tag{66}$$

Expressions (66) and (64) are approximately the same when

$$x'/l(u_0) \gg (x')^2/L_s^2,$$

i.e.
$$L_s^2 \gg xl(u_0). \tag{67}$$

The condition (63), i.e. $L_s^2 \gg xl(u)$ is that which determines whether or not the anisotropy is weak. The two conditions lead to quite different answers if $l(u) \ll l(u_0)$. In this case the condition $L_s^2 \gg xl(u)$ is not sufficient for the applicability of the age equation.

(d) Remark on age theory

The age is not a unique characterization of the energy; neutrons of the same energy have different ages in different media.

The boundary conditions, namely that the flux and current are continuous, involve different values of the age at the interface of two media. In general numerical methods have to be used to solve such a problem.

7.3 The neutron distribution at large distances from the source

In the previous section it was shown that if $L_s^2 \gg xl(u_0)$ then the neutron distribution has a Gaussian shape. In neutron-shielding problems one is interested in the penetration of neutrons to much larger distances than $L_s^2/l(u_0)$. The age equation is derived on the assumption that the neutron distribution is nearly isotropic. This is no longer true when one is interested in the neutrons which have penetrated to large distances, because the neutrons which do reach these distances suffer very small deflections and consequently small energy changes over a greater part of their path. If the mean free path varies with the neutron energy and has its largest value at an energy E_1, then the neutrons which penetrate to a large distance are those which are slowed down to energies near to E_1 and then proceed without a further collision to regions far from the source.

It is obvious that methods of calculation different from those described in the previous chapters have to be used. The methods of calculation can be divided into two types—analytic calculations for specific variations of mean free path with energy, and numerical calculations which require the use of a large digital computer. There are also some empirical methods, which will be mentioned at the end of this section. A detailed discussion of the analytical methods is given in Davison's book; only a brief outline will be given here, with a statement of the results. The numerical calculations are described briefly also, as space does not permit a detailed discussion.

(a) The case of constant mean free path

In all of these calculations the neutron density due to a plane source in an infinite elastically scattering medium is determined. It was shown in Chapter 3, Section 3.4 that the distribution due to a point source can be calculated from that due to a plane source and consequently $N_0(\mathbf{r}, v)$ can be determined for any source distribution.

We shall consider the density as a function of the velocity v and not E the energy or its associated variable u the lethargy. This may seem inconsistent as we have considered N as a function of E or u in the previous sections, and we shall continue to use these variables in later chapters. The reason for the choice of v is as follows. The following three Sections 7.3 (a), 7.3 (b) and 7.3 (c) contain a brief summary of the calculation of the neutron distribution at large distances: they consist in the main of a statement of results. For all the details of the analysis the reader would have to consult either the papers by Verde and Wick [35, 36], who use the lethargy as a variable, or Davison's book [1]. The latter would seem to be the more profitable course as a comparison is made there of several methods. He uses the velocity as the variable, and we have used it here in order to help the reader who wishes to consult Davison's book for more details.

The velocity-dependent transport equation for plane geometry is given by

$$v\mu \frac{\partial N(x, v, \mu)}{\partial x} + v\Sigma N(x, v, \mu) =$$

$$\iint c(v')\Sigma(v')v'N(x, v', \mu')f(v', \Omega' \longrightarrow v, \Omega) \, dv' \, d\Omega'$$

$$+ \frac{1}{4\pi} \delta(x)\delta(v - v_0), \quad (68)$$

where v_0 is the initial velocity of the neutron and the scattering function $f(v', \Omega' \longrightarrow v, \Omega)$ for a medium containing nuclei of atomic weight A is given by Chapter 1, equation (16). f is given by the formula

$$f = \frac{(A + 1)^2 v}{4\pi A(v')^2} \delta[\mu_0 - \tfrac{1}{2}(A + 1)(v/v') + \tfrac{1}{2}(A - 1)(v'/v)]. \quad (69)$$

The other symbols have been defined previously. The source emits neutrons of velocity v_0 and is situated at $x = 0$.

In some analyses the functions $N(x, v, \mu)$ and f are expanded in series of spherical harmonics, i.e.

$$N(x, v, \mu) = \frac{1}{4\pi} \sum_{n=0}^{\infty} (2n + 1)N_n(x, v)P_n(\mu), \quad (70)$$

and $\quad f(v', \Omega' \longrightarrow v, \Omega) = \frac{1}{4\pi} \sum_{n=0}^{\infty} (2n + 1)f_n(v', v)P_n(\mu_0). \quad (71)$

The coefficients $f_n(v', v)$ are determined easily. They are given by

$$f_n(v', v) = \frac{(A + 1)^2 v}{4\pi A(v')^2} P_n[\tfrac{1}{2}(A + 1)(v/v') - \tfrac{1}{2}(A - 1)(v'/v)]. \quad (72)$$

The series (70) and (71) are substituted into the integral term on the right-hand side of (68). The cross multiplication of these series results in integrals of the type

$$\int P_n(\mu')P_m(\mu_0) \, d\Omega'.$$

101

Now $\cos^{-1} \mu_0$ is the angle between Ω and Ω', then

$$P_n(\mu_0) = P_n(\mu)P_n(\mu') + 2 \sum_{m=1}^{n} \frac{(n+m)!}{(n-m)!} P_n{}^m(\mu)P_n{}^m(\mu') \cos m(\phi - \phi'),$$

where $P_n{}^m(\mu)$ are the associated Legendre functions [13]. Therefore,

$$\int P_n(\mu')P_m(\mu_0) \, d\Omega' = \frac{4\pi}{2n+1} P_n(\mu)\delta_{nm},$$

where δ_{nm} is the Kronecker δ symbol, i.e. $\delta_{nm} = 1$ for $n = m$, and is zero otherwise. The integral term of (68) becomes

$$\frac{c\Sigma}{4\pi} \sum_{n=0}^{\infty} (2n+1)P_n(\mu)\int_{v}^{v(1-q)^{-\frac{1}{2}}} v'f_n(v', v)N_n(x, v') \, dv'. \tag{73}$$

Equation (68) is multiplied by $P_n(\mu)$ and integrated over Ω. The following set of equations is obtained for the $N_n(x, v)$:

$$(n+1)v \frac{\partial N_{n+1}(x, v)}{\partial x} + nv \frac{\partial N_{n-1}(x, v)}{\partial x} + (2n+1)v\Sigma N_n(x, v)$$
$$= (2n+1)c\Sigma \int_{v}^{v(1-q^2)^{-\frac{1}{2}}} v'f_n(v', v)N_n(x, v') \, dv' + \delta_{n0}\delta(v - v_0). \tag{74}$$

In order to solve the set of equations (74) the Fourier transform is taken with respect to the spatial co-ordinate x, and the Mellin transform with respect to the velocity. Let

$$\Pi_n(w, \eta) = (v_0)^{-\eta} \int_0^{v_0} v^{\eta-1} \, dv \int_{-\infty}^{+\infty} N_n(x, v) \exp(iwx) \, dx. \tag{75}$$

Multiply equation (74) by $v^{\eta-2} \exp(iwx)$ and integrate over all x and v from 0 to v_0. The following set of equations is obtained for the $\Pi_n(w, \eta)$:

$$iw[(n+1)\Pi_{n+1}(w, \eta) + n\Pi_{n-1}(w, \eta)]$$
$$+ (2n+1)\Sigma[1 - g_n(\eta)]\Pi_n(w, \eta) = v_0^{-2}\delta_{n0}, \tag{76}$$
where

$$g_n(\eta) = -c \int_{(A-1)/(A+1)}^{1} y^{-1}P_n\left[\frac{(A+1)y^2 - (A-1)}{2y}\right] dy. \tag{77}$$

The transform of the integral term on the right-hand side of (74) is obtained by altering first the order of integration with respect to v' and v.

102

It can be seen that η appears only as a parameter in the equations. This is only true in this particular case, where the cross-section is independent of energy.

Waller [34] has shown that (76) can be solved and that the solution for $\Pi_0(w, \eta)$ can be expressed as the continued fraction

$$\Pi_0(w, \eta) = \frac{\Sigma^{-1}v_0^{-2}}{1 - g_0(\eta)} + \frac{w^2\Sigma^{-2}}{3[1 - g_1(\eta)]} + \frac{4w^2\Sigma^{-2}}{5[1 - g_2(\eta)]} \cdots (78)$$

The main problem in the analysis is, of course, the inversion of the transform $\Pi_0(w, \eta)$. This can be achieved using the method of residues and the saddle-point method. However, the method which has been outlined has one drawback. To obtain the function $N_0(x, v)$ for very large values of x requires the evaluation of a large number of the $g_n(\eta)$. This is due to the fact that the angular distribution $N(x, v, \mu)$ is anisotropic at large distances, and the terms of series (70) tend to become equal for large x. Other analytical methods have been devised to avoid this difficulty. The methods are still based, however, on the use of the Fourier and Mellin transforms. Wick [35] obtained the following expression for the density $N_0(x, v)$:

$$B[x \ln (v_0/v)]^{-\frac{1}{4}} \exp \left[-\Sigma \mid x \mid + 2\{A\Sigma k_1 \mid x \mid \ln (v_0/v)\}^{\frac{1}{2}} \right.$$
$$\left. + \eta^* \ln (v_0/v)], \quad (79)$$

where B, k_1 and η^* are constants depending on the atomic weight A.

It can be seen from the form of the expression for $N_0(x, v)$ that the spectrum is changing with the distance x, i.e. an equilibrium spectrum is not obtained at very large distances. This is the feature of the constant mean free path case.

(b) The case of the variable mean free path

The analysis which has been given in the previous section can be extended to the case where the quantities Σ and c vary with velocity. The variable η appeared as a parameter in equations (76). However, for the case of variable mean free path this is no longer true. Suppose that the medium is non-capturing and that the variation of the mean free path with velocity is given by the following formula:

$$l(v) = [\Sigma(v)]^{-1} = l(v_0)\sum B_j(v/v_0)^{\beta_j}, \quad (80)$$

where β_j and B_j are some constants. The Fourier–Mellin transforms are given by the following instead of (75):

$$\Pi_n(w, \eta) = v_0^{-\eta} \int_0^{v_0} v^{\eta-1} \, dv \int_{-\infty}^{+\infty} [l(v)]^{-1} N_n(x, v) \exp(iwx) \, dx.$$

The following equations are obtained for the $\Pi_n(w, \eta)$:

$$iwl(v_0) \sum_j B_j [(n+1)\Pi_{n+1}(w, \eta + \beta_j) + n\Pi_{n-1}(w, \eta + \beta_j)]$$
$$+ (2n+1)[1 - g_n(\eta)]\Pi_n(w, \eta) = v_0^{-2}\delta_{n0}. \quad (81)$$

Verde and Wick [36] have calculated $N_0(x, v)$ for small v when

$$\lim_{v \to 0} l(v) = 0. \quad (82)$$

This implies that the β_j in formula (80) are positive. They found that $N_0(x, v)$ has the following form for large x:

$$[\,|x|/l(v_0)]^{-1-\gamma} \exp[-|x|/l(v_0)]G(v, \mu),$$

where γ is positive and $G(v, \mu)$ some function of v and μ. It can be seen that there is an equilibrium spectrum at large distances.

(c) Numerical solutions

The neutron distribution can be found using the Monte Carlo method. In this method the life histories of particular neutrons are traced in the medium. Using tables of random numbers the point of collision along a given track, for example, can be determined by sampling from a given probability distribution. If a sufficiently large number of histories is followed, then the neutron distribution can be obtained. The accuracy with which it is determined depends on the number of histories which has been followed. The main difficulty in applying the method to shielding problems is that the number of neutrons found at large distances in a given velocity interval is small compared with the output from the source. However, there are techniques for avoiding this difficulty. The Monte Carlo method can be used when the angular distribution in scattering is anisotropic, and when the cross-sections depend on the energy in a complicated way.

There is another type of numerical method—the moment solution —which is suitable for the velocity equation (68). The starting point is the set of equations (74). The analysis need not be restricted to the

104

use of the scattering law (69) and the integral term on the right-hand side of (74) can be replaced by a more general one,

$$(2n + 1)\int_0^{v_0} v' N_n(x, v') f_n(v' \longrightarrow v) \, dv',$$

where $f_n(v' \longrightarrow v)$ is a function which may have been determined experimentally and is given numerically. Let the spatial moments of $N_n(x, v')$ be defined as follows:

$$M_{nl} = (l!)^{-1} \int_{-\infty}^{+\infty} x^l N_n(x, v) \, dx. \tag{83}$$

Equation (74) is multiplied by $x^l/(l!)$ and integrated over x. A set of linear inhomogeneous equations is obtained for the $M_{nl}(v)$. It is then possible to construct the function $N_n(x, v)$ from the spatial moments $M_{nl}(v)$. For more details of this very powerful method the reader should consult the book by Goldstein [37].

(d) Empirical formulae

In practice the total neutron cross-sections show a general tendency to increase with decreasing energy. The calculation of the flux inside a shield placed around a nuclear reactor can be divided into three stages. The first stage of the calculation consists in the determination of the variation of the flux of fast neutrons (i.e. energy greater than 0·5 MeV), with distance into the shield. The second step consists in the calculation of the flux of neutrons of lower energy arising from the fast group and the last step consists of the estimation of the thermal flux distribution.

Neutrons are slowed down rapidly by collisions with hydrogen and by inelastic collisions with heavy elements. The inelastic cross-section may be as much as one half of the total cross-section for energies greater than 0·5 MeV. The calculation of Verde and Wick showed that the attenuation of the neutron flux is determined by the mean free path at the incident energy for large distances where the mean free path decreases with increasing energy. In the present problem inelastic scattering in the heavy elements causes a more rapid degradation of neutron energy than in an elastically scattering medium. Therefore the decay of the neutron distribution with distance from the source will approach an exponential decay more rapidly. The total cross-section acts as though it were all pure absorption, and can be regarded, therefore, as a removal cross-section.

The elastic scattering of fast neutrons may be anisotropic in the laboratory system. The anisotropy of the scattering was discussed in a qualitative manner in Chapter 1, Section 1.4, where it was shown that the scattering of neutrons by the heavier nuclei in a shield will be anisotropic for neutron energies of the order of several MeV.

The true removal cross-section is less than the total cross-section. Spinney [38] estimated it as equal to the total cross-section less the cross-section for forward scattering. He suggested that a rough estimate of Σ_{rem} could be obtained from the analogy of a transport cross-section, by writing

$$\Sigma_{rem}(E) = \Sigma(E) - 2\pi \int_{-1}^{+1} \mu\, \Sigma_s(E, \mu)\, d\mu, \tag{84}$$

where $\Sigma_s(E, \mu)$ is the differential cross-section for elastic scattering of neutrons of energy E through an angle $\cos^{-1}\mu$. There are some experimental estimates of $\Sigma_s(E, \mu)$ and where data are lacking theoretical estimates are used.

If the source neutrons have a spectrum $S(E)$, then the flux of neutrons in the fast group will vary with distance according to the formula

$$\phi(x) = \int S(E) \exp\left[-\Sigma_{rem}(E)x\right] dE. \tag{85}$$

For more details of this empirical method the reader should consult the book by Price, Horton and Spinney [38].

106

CHAPTER 8

The Numerical Solution of the Energy Dependent Transport Equation

8.1 The Monte Carlo method

Some of the methods used in the solution of the one group equation can be generalized to solve the energy dependent transport equation, e.g. the multi-group spherical harmonics method. However, some of these methods then become very complicated from an algebraic point of view. This chapter is restricted to some remarks about the Monte Carlo method, followed by descriptions of the Carlson method and multi-group diffusion theory. These direct numerical methods have proved to be most useful in practice. A description of perturbation theory is included at the end of the chapter.

In the previous chapter the use was mentioned of the Monte Carlo method in shielding problems. In the shielding problem the fraction of neutrons which passes through a very thick layer of absorbing material has to be determined. It can be used also in the study of criticality problems. The time constant of a super-critical system can be determined by following the build-up of successive generations of neutrons in the system. The critical size can be obtained by determining the time constant for several sizes of system and then the critical dimensions can be obtained by interpolation for zero time constant. In all these problems the histories of a sufficient number of neutrons is followed from collision to collision. In going from one collision to another the problem is to determine

(i) the distance travelled before the next collision takes place;
(ii) the type of collision which then takes place and the energy and direction of the neutron after the collision.

The distance which a neutron travels from one collision to the next depends on its mean free path l, which is a function of the neutron

107

energy and the material in which it is moving. The probability $p(x)$ that a collision takes place in the interval x to $x + dx$ is given by,

$$p(x)\, dx = \exp\left[-x/l\right] (dx/l), \tag{1}$$

$$= -dy, \tag{2}$$

where
$$y = \exp\left[-x/l\right]. \tag{3}$$

y varies between 0 and 1, and from (2) it can be seen that it is distributed uniformly in this range. The value of y can be obtained, therefore, by making a choice between 0 and 1, using a set of random numbers. The distance x travelled by the neutron is determined then from (3). If the neutron track crosses a boundary into another medium, then a new path length must be determined from the point where it enters the second medium with the aid of a new random number. If the boundary is a free surface the neutron is lost, of course, from the system.

Let $p_i(E)[1 \leqslant i \leqslant k]$ be the probability that a process of type i takes place when a neutron of energy E undergoes a collision. Then $\sum_{i=1}^{k} p_i(E) = 1$. In order to sample for a particular type of collision one can proceed as follows. Let R be a random number chosen in the range $(0, 1)$.

If $\sum_{i=1}^{s} p_i(E) \leqslant R \leqslant \sum_{i=1}^{s+1} p_i(E)$, then a collision of type s can be regarded as having taken place, i.e. the interval 0 to 1 has been divided up into a set of sub-intervals of width $p_i(E)$. One can also devise simple ways of sampling from an energy and angular distribution. Thus the history of a particular neutron can be determined.

In order to carry out a Monte Carlo calculation a stock of random numbers is required. A sequence of random numbers can be generated by a suitable recurrence relation. For example, a sequence can be generated by the following relation:

$$R_{n+1} = AR_n \ (\text{modulo } m) \tag{4}$$

where A and m are constants whose choice depends on the digital computer which is used.‡ There are several tests which can be made to ensure the randomness of a given sequence of numbers.

The Monte Carlo method has been used in the calculation of the resonance escape probability in a thermal reactor. This problem was

‡ i.e. R_{n+1} is obtained by rejecting the first m digits from the product AR_n.

discussed in Chapter 6, where various empirical methods were described. The calculation of the resonance escape probability in a reactor from the basic cross-section data is very difficult for the case where the reactor core has a heterogeneous structure, consisting of a lattice of fuel rods surrounded by moderating material. The difficulty arises from the complicated resonance structure of the absorption cross-section in the fuel. There are about one hundred of these resonances between 6·7 eV (the lowest) and 1 keV in uranium 238, and above this energy many are unresolved. Although these factors complicate the application of the Monte Carlo method it is still possible to carry out calculations. An idea of the amount of work which is entailed is provided by the following example. Richtmeyer [39] calculated the resonance escape probability for 0·6″ diameter rods space 1·1″ apart in a hexagonal array in water. He considered about 10,000 neutron case histories and obtained $(1 - p)$ to within 1%. [N.B. $p \sim 0.85$.]

Returning to the shielding problem, the attenuation through a typical neutron shield may be 10^{-10}. It would be impossible to calculate such a quantity by the Monte Carlo method by tracking at least 10^{10} neutrons from the source. Some form of weighting technique has to be employed. For example, the neutron's weight immediately after a collision may be obtained by multiplying its previous weight by the expected number of secondary neutrons occurring at the collision.

Various other techniques can be used to increase the efficiency of the Monte Carlo method. There is the antithetic variate technique which has been used most successfully in the evaluation of multidimensional integrals. For further details on these topics it is suggested that the reader should consult the following references [40, 41].

8.2 Multi-group theory

In multi-group theory the energy range is divided into a number of intervals or groups. In each interval it is assumed that the cross-sections are given by averaged values. The energy dependence of a particular cross-section is approximated, therefore, by means of a series of steps.

The choice of the energy groups depends on the physics of the problem. For example, a two-group representation is quite adequate for the calculation of some properties of a thermal reactor. In such a reactor the bulk of the neutrons is at thermal energy. One group can be chosen to represent these neutrons. The second group represents the epithermal tail in which the spectrum is given by dE/E. In other calculations the energy groups may be chosen such that a division between two groups corresponds to the threshold for a particular reaction. In some fast reactor calculations, the threshold for fast fission of uranium 238, ~ 1 MeV, is chosen as such a dividing energy.

In order to obtain an averaged cross-section for a process in a particular group it is necessary to know the neutron spectrum within the group. The spectrum may be known in certain problems, e.g. in the epithermal group in the two group calculation for a thermal system. If the spectrum and cross-sections are fairly smooth function of energy, no problem arises if a sufficient number of groups is taken, as the variation in a particular group can be inferred from the histogram representing the spectrum. The transfer probabilities from group to group must be specified also. Suppose that the scattering is isotropic and that the probability for scattering from an energy E' to the energy interval E to $E + dE$ is given by

$$\left(\frac{1}{4\pi}\right) f(E' \longrightarrow E)\, dE. \tag{5}$$

In the multi-group formulation the following integrals appear:

$$\int_{E_{i-1}}^{E_i} f(E' \longrightarrow E)\, dE, \tag{6}$$

where $[E_{i-1}, E_i]$ is a particular energy interval. It can be postulated that each of the integrals (6) can be approximated by a step function,

i.e. $\quad \int_{E_{i-1}}^{E_i} f(E' \longrightarrow E)\, dE = f_{j \rightarrow i}$ for $E_j > E' > E_{j-1}$,

where $f_{j \rightarrow i}$ are some constants and they satisfy the normalization condition

$$\sum_i f_{j \rightarrow i} = 1. \tag{7}$$

This assumption can be criticized as follows. In an elastic collision with a nucleus of atomic weight A, a neutron of energy E' will be scattered into the energy range $E' > E > \left(\dfrac{A-1}{A+1}\right)^2 E'$. Therefore, the actual value of the integral (6) is not constant for E' in the range E_i to E_{i+1}. In order to avoid this difficulty an approach such as the following could be adopted. Consider the energy dependent Boltzmann equation in plane geometry with the scattering law given by (5), i.e.

$$\mu \frac{\partial \Psi(x, E, \mu)}{\partial x} + \Sigma(E)\Psi(x, E, \mu) =$$
$$= \frac{1}{4\pi} \int \Phi(x, E')\Sigma(E')f(E' \longrightarrow E)\, dE', \quad (8)$$

where $\Phi(x, E)$ is the flux and $\Psi(x, E, \mu)$ is the angular distribution of flux.

One now assumes that in the group $[E_{i-1}, E_i]$, $\Psi(x, E, \mu)$ and $\Phi(x, E)$ can be written as

$$\Psi(x, E, \mu) = B_i(E)\Psi_i(x, \mu)$$

and
$$\Phi(x, E) = B_i(E)\phi_i(x).\ddagger$$

$$\left. \begin{array}{c} \\ \\ \\ \end{array} \right\} \quad (9)$$

Let
$$b_i = \int_{E_{i-1}}^{E_i} B_i(E)\, dE.$$

The following equation is obtained for the neutrons in group i when equation (8) is integrated over the energy interval E_{i-1} to E_i.

$$\mu\, b_i \frac{\partial \psi_i(x, \mu)}{\partial x} + b_i \Sigma_i \psi_i(x, \mu)$$
$$= \frac{1}{4\pi} \int_{E_{i-1}}^{E_i} \sum_j \phi_j(x) \int_{E_{j-1}}^{E_j} B_j(E')\Sigma(E')f(E' \longrightarrow E)\, dE'\, dE,$$

$$= \frac{1}{4\pi} \sum_j b_j f_{j \rightarrow i} \phi_j(x), \quad (10)$$

where

$$b_i \Sigma_i = \int_{E_{i-1}}^{E_i} \Sigma(E)B_i(E)\, dE, \quad (11)$$

and

$$b_j f_{j \rightarrow i} = \int_{E_{i-1}}^{E_i} \int_{E_{j-1}}^{E_j} B_j(E')\Sigma(E')f(E' \longrightarrow E)\, dE'\, dE. \quad (12)$$

$b_i \phi_i(x)$ is the total flux of neutrons in the energy interval $[E_{i-1}, E_i]$.

‡ For a large system one could assume that the spectrum was equal to that in an infinite medium.

The energy spectrum of the flux in a group has been assumed to be independent of x. This may be true in a large reactor core at points which are distant from a boundary. In order to calculate the $f_{j \to i}$ the spectrum $B(E)$ has to be estimated. A more detailed discussion of all these questions is given in Davison's book.

Selengut [24] has discussed also the derivation of the few group equations from the energy dependent diffusion equation. He obtains equations of the conventional form with the important difference that the group constants are weighted by the product of both the adjoint and the direct flux.

The energy groups should be chosen such that the cross-sections are reasonably constant in each energy interval. It is not always possible to do this as the cross-sections may have a resonance structure, and in one energy interval there may be several resonances. The spectrum in a group will dip at the energies corresponding to the peaks of the resonances. In some calculations the spectrum is assumed to be given by $1/\sigma_t$, where σ_t is the total cross-section, i.e. by the narrow resonance formula discussed in Chapter 6, Section 6.4.

Therefore, an effective cross-section $\overline{\sigma}_x(E)$ for a particular process x is given by the formula

$$\overline{\sigma}_x(E) = \frac{\displaystyle\int_{E_{i-1}}^{E_i} (\sigma_x/\sigma_t) \, dE}{\displaystyle\int_{E_{i-1}}^{E_i} (1/\sigma_t) \, dE}. \tag{13}$$

The Doppler effect is due to the change of the effective cross-sections with the temperature.

8.3 Carlson S_n method

This is a numerical method for solving problems in plane, spherical and cylindrical geometry, and is intended for use with high speed digital computing machines. This method was originally developed for the case of isotropic scattering although it has been extended subsequently to take account of anisotropic scattering. The method originally took account of anisotropic scattering by using the transport cross-section as defined in Chapter 2, Section 2.1, i.e.

$$\sigma_{tr} = \sigma_s \left[1 - \int_{-1}^{+1} \mu f_e(\mu) \, d\mu \right], \tag{14}$$

where μ is the cosine of the angle between the initial and final directions of the neutron, and $f_e(\mu)$ is the angular distribution of scattered neutrons.

(a) Original S_n method [42]

Consider the energy dependent Boltzmann equation in multi-group form for the case of spherical symmetry and isotropic scattering. Let the suffix i denote a particular energy group. The angular distribution of flux $\psi_i(r, \mu)$ for the group i satisfies an equation

$$\left[\mu \frac{\partial}{\partial r} + \frac{(1 - \mu^2)}{r} \frac{\partial}{\partial \mu} + \Sigma_i(r)\right]\psi_i(r, \mu) = S_i(r), \tag{15}$$

where r is the distance from the centre of the system and $\cos^{-1} \mu$ is the angle between Ω and the radius vector $\mathbf{r}$. The source term $S_i(r)$ in equation (15) takes the form

$$\frac{1}{4\pi} \sum_j \Sigma_{ji} \phi_j(r) + g_i, \tag{16}$$

where Σ_{ji} are the group transfer cross-sections and $\phi_j(r)$ is the flux in the group j.‡ g_i is the number of fission neutrons emitted in the group,

i.e. $$g_i = \frac{1}{4\pi} G_i \sum_j \Sigma_{jf} \phi_j(r),$$

where Σ_{jf} is the macroscopic fission cross-section in group j and G_i is the fraction of fission neutrons emitted in group i.

The case of spherical symmetry is considered because the original application of the method was in the calculation of the reactivity of a spherical system, the simplest example being a bare fissile sphere.

Carlson divides the range of integration over μ into N (usually equal) sub-intervals. Let the points defining these sub-intervals be $\mu_n(n = 0, 1, \ldots N)$, so that $\mu_0 = -1$, $\mu_N = 1$. The number of intervals N defines the order of the approximation.

In the sub-interval between μ_{n-1} and μ_n, $\psi_i(r, \mu)$ is assumed to be linear in μ, i.e.

$$\psi_i(r, \mu) = \frac{\mu - \mu_{n-1}}{\mu_n - \mu_{n-1}} \psi_i(r, \mu_n) + \frac{\mu_n - \mu}{\mu_n - \mu_{n-1}} \psi_i(r, \mu_{n-1}). \tag{17}$$

‡ $\Sigma_{ji} = f_{j \to i}$ as defined in (12).

113

Equation (15) is integrated over μ from μ_{n-1} to μ_n, assuming that $\psi_i(r, \mu)$ is given by (17), and the following equation is obtained

$$[a_n \frac{\partial}{\partial r} + \frac{b_n}{r} + \Sigma_i(r)]\psi_i(r, \mu_n)$$

$$+ \left[a'_n \frac{\partial}{\partial r} - \frac{b_n}{r} + \Sigma_i(r)\right]\psi_i(r, \mu_{n-1}) = 2S_i(r), \quad (18)$$

where
$$a_n = \tfrac{1}{3}(2\mu_n + \mu_{n-1}),$$
$$a'_n = \tfrac{1}{3}(\mu_n + 2\mu_{n-1}),$$
$$b_n = 2(3 - \mu^2_n - \mu_n\mu_{n-1} - \mu^2_{n-1})/3(\mu_n - \mu_{n-1}).$$

The ϕ_i occurring in $S_i(r)$ are calculated from the relation

$$\phi_i(r) = 2\pi \int_{-1}^{+1} \psi_i(r, \mu) \, d\mu.$$

There are, therefore, N differential equations to calculate the $(N + 1)$ functions $\psi_i(r, \mu_n)$. These are supplemented by an additional equation obtained by putting $\mu = -1$ in equation (15) giving

$$\left[-\frac{\partial}{\partial r} + \Sigma_i(r)\right]\psi_i(r, -1) = S_i(r). \quad (19)$$

The technique of solving equations (18) and (19) is to assume some source function $S_i(r)$ for each energy group i and then to integrate equation (19) over r numerically from the outer boundary, to the centre of the system, using the boundary condition of no inward neutron flux at the outer surface $r = b$, i.e. $\psi_i(b, \mu) = 0$ for $\mu < 0$. The integration over r is done similarly to that over μ. The r range is divided into intervals $[r_{m-1}, r_m]$, and $\psi_i(r, \mu_n)$ is assumed to be linear in each interval. Equation (19) is integrated over the range $[r_{m-1}, r_m]$, taking an average value of $\Sigma_i(r)$ in each interval and replacing r^{-1} by $2(r_{m-1} + r_m)^{-1}$.

Having calculated $\psi_i(r, -1) = \psi_i(r, \mu_0)$, equation (18) for $n = 1$ is solved for $\psi_i(r, \mu_1)$, again integrating inwards, and one proceeds in this manner until $\psi_i(r, 0)$ is obtained. To determine $\psi_i(r, \mu_n)$ for $\mu_n > 0$, one starts from the centre and integrates outwards, using the central condition of symmetry:

$$\psi_i(0, -\mu) = \psi_i(0, \mu). \quad (20)$$

114

Having calculated the $\psi_i(r, \mu)$ from a guessed S_i in each group, new values S_i are calculated from

$$S_i = \frac{1}{4\pi} \sum_j \Sigma_{ji}\phi_j(r) + g_i.$$

This process is repeated until a desired agreement is reached on comparing two successive iterations point by point. The ratio of $S_i(r)$ for successive iterations will then be equal to a factor independent of i and r. This factor is called the multiplication. If the problem is the determination of a critical dimension of the system, e.g. the core radius, then the calculation is repeated with various values of the core radius, and the critical radius is determined for which the multiplication is unity.

The fundamental idea in Carlson's method is the manner in which equations (18) and (19) are solved in order to ensure the stability of the numerical process. The following physical arguments can be advanced in favour of the methods described above. Consider a thin layer of material containing a source distribution S. Let ϕ_1 be the flux of neutrons incident on one of its surfaces and ϕ_2 the emergent flux. Then

$$\phi_2 = \alpha\phi_1 + \beta S,$$

where α is the attenuation factor for the incident neutrons and β is the fraction of source neutrons escaping.

If ϕ_2 is determined from ϕ_1, any error in ϕ_1 will be reduced in ϕ_2 since α is less than unity, whereas if ϕ_1 is determined from ϕ_2 (as by integrating against the direction of the neutron flow) the errors will accumulate.

In the case of a spherical system, negative values of μ correspond to directions towards the centre, and positive values to directions away from the centre. The value of $\mu(=\mathbf{r} . \mathbf{\Omega}/r)$ will increase as the neutron proceeds along a particular neutron path approaching the centre but not passing through it. Therefore, in order to integrate along the direction of the neutron flow, the integration over r must be performed towards the centre for negative μ and away from the centre for positive μ, starting with the values of $\phi_i(r, \mu)$ for $\mu = -1$.

(b) Discrete S_n method

Improved versions of the S_n method have been developed by Carlson [43]. One of these is called the discrete S_n method. In order to solve equation (15) a set of cells A_{mn} is introduced as before, i.e. r is represented by a set $\{r_m\}$, and μ by a set $\{\mu_n\}$, with $0 \leqslant r \leqslant a$ and $-1 \leqslant \mu \leqslant +1$; a is the outer radius of the system. As before Carlson takes an even number of equal intervals $\mu_n = 1 - 2n/N$, $n = 0, 1, \ldots N$. He denotes the mid-point of an interval by $\bar{\mu}_n$, i.e. $\bar{\mu}_n = -1 + (2n - 1)/N$, where $n = 1, 2, \ldots N$. The $\bar{\mu}_n$ are basically the discrete directions of the method, and are given equal weights $1/N$. A set of difference equations is deduced for the values of the flux at the points $\bar{\mu}_n$.

Let
$$\Delta_m = r_m - r_{m-1},$$
$$\Delta_n = \mu_n - \mu_{n-1},$$
$$\delta_m = \Delta_m/r'_m,$$
where
$$r'_m = 2(r^3_m - r^3_{m-1})/3(r^2_m - r^2_{m-1}). \tag{22}$$

Let the average of $(1 - \mu^2)$ be denoted by γ_n which will be determined later.

Carlson assumes that
$$\overline{\psi}_{m, n} = \tfrac{1}{2}[\psi_{m-\frac{1}{2}, n} + \psi_{m-\frac{1}{2}, n-1}],$$
$$= \tfrac{1}{2}[\psi_{m, n-\frac{1}{2}} + \psi_{m-1, n-\frac{1}{2}}],$$

where the suffixes $(m - \frac{1}{2})$, $(n - \frac{1}{2})$ denote the mid-points of the ranges $[r_m, r_{m-1}]$ and $[\mu_n, \mu_{n-1}]$ respectively. $\psi(r, \mu)$ has been assumed to be the linear over A_{mn} in the variables μ and r.

Equation (15) is averaged over A_{mn} to form a difference equation

$$\bar{\mu}_n[\psi_{m, n-\frac{1}{2}} - \psi_{m-1, n-\frac{1}{2}}] + \gamma_n\delta_m[\psi_{m, n-\frac{1}{2}} + \psi_{m-1, n-\frac{1}{2}}$$
$$- 2\psi_{m-\frac{1}{2}, n-1}] + \tfrac{1}{2}\Sigma_m\Delta_m[\psi_{m, n-\frac{1}{2}} + \psi_{m-1, n-\frac{1}{2}}] = \Delta_m S_m. \tag{23}$$

Equation (23) can be re-arranged to give

$$[\bar{\mu}_n + \gamma_n\delta_m + \tfrac{1}{2}\Sigma_m\Delta_m]\psi_{m, n-\frac{1}{2}} + [-\bar{\mu}_n + \gamma_n\delta_m$$
$$+ \tfrac{1}{2}\Sigma_m\Delta_m]\psi_{m-1, n-\frac{1}{2}} = \Delta_m S_m + 2\gamma_n\delta_m\psi_{m-\frac{1}{2}, n-1}. \tag{24}$$

In equations (23) and (24) the suffix i which denotes the particular energy group has been dropped. The recurrence relations are solved for $n = 1, \ldots N$. Before this can be done $\psi_{m-\frac{1}{2}, 0}$ has to be calculated from equation (19), which is identical to (24) when $\bar{\mu} = -1$ and $\gamma_n = 0$. In the evaluation of (24) one solves for $\psi_{m-1, n-\frac{1}{2}}$ if $\bar{\mu}_n$ is negative and for $\psi_{m, n-\frac{1}{2}}$ if $\bar{\mu}_n$ is positive. $\bar{\mu}_n$ need not be the mid-point of a chosen μ interval. Modified values of $\bar{\mu}$ can be determined such that

$$\frac{1}{N} \sum_n | \bar{\mu}_n |^2 = \tfrac{1}{3}.$$

If this is done then the diffusion theory approximation is satisfied exactly.

The values of γ_n [average of $(1 - \mu^2)$] and $(r_m')^{-1}$ [average of r^{-1}] are chosen such that certain conservation conditions are satisfied. To determine the values of γ equation (15) is written as follows

$$\mu \frac{\partial \psi}{\partial r} + \frac{1}{r} \frac{\partial}{\partial \mu} [(1 - \mu^2)\psi] + \frac{2}{r} \mu\psi + \Sigma\psi = S. \tag{25}$$

Equation (25) is integrated over μ from -1 to $+1$. Then

$$\frac{\partial j}{\partial r} + \frac{2}{r} j + \Sigma\phi = 4\pi S, \tag{26}$$

where the current $\quad j(r) = 2\pi \int_{-1}^{+1} \mu\psi(r, \mu) \, d\mu.$

(26) is approximated by the following difference equations

$$[j_m - j_{m-1}] + \delta_m[j_m + j_{m-1}] + \Sigma_m \Delta_m \phi_{m-\frac{1}{2}} = 4\pi \Delta_m S_m. \tag{27}$$

It is necessary that equation (23) when summed over n and multiplied by $\frac{4\pi}{N}$ should be equal to (27). This is true provided that

$$j_m + j_{m-1} = \frac{4\pi}{N} \sum_n \gamma_n [\psi_{m-\frac{1}{2}, n} - \psi_{m-\frac{1}{2}, n-1}]. \tag{28}$$

The left-hand side of equation (28) is equal to

$$\frac{4\pi}{N} \sum \bar{\mu}_n[\psi_{m, n-\frac{1}{2}} + \psi_{m-1, n-\frac{1}{2}}] = \frac{4\pi}{N} \sum \bar{\mu}_n[\psi_{m-\frac{1}{2}, n} + \psi_{m-\frac{1}{2}, n-1}],$$

$$= \frac{4\pi}{N} \sum \psi_{m-\frac{1}{2}, n-1}[\bar{\mu}_n + \bar{\mu}_{n-1}].$$

Therefore, (28) implies that

$$\gamma_n - \gamma_{n-1} = -\bar{\mu}_n - \bar{\mu}_{n-1}, \tag{29}$$

and $\qquad\qquad \gamma_1 = -\bar{\mu}_1.$

The formula for the average value of r^{-1} in an interval Δ_m can be obtained similarly by writing $\dfrac{\partial j}{\partial r} + \dfrac{2}{r} j$ as $r^{-2} \, \partial(r^2 j)/\partial r$ in (26).

This form of the Carlson method is the basis of the one-dimensional code DSN and the two-dimensional code TDC [44].

(c) Plane geometry

The equations for plane geometry can be obtained from those for spherical geometry by putting $b_n = 0$ in equations (18).

(d) Anisotropic S_n method

An anisotropic version of the S_n method exists and it is possible to take into account the transport of neutrons in hydrogenous substances.

When anisotropic scattering is taken into account the Boltzmann transport equation in the multi-group approximation and in spherical geometry can be written

$$\mu \frac{\partial \psi_i(r, \mu)}{\partial r} + \frac{(1 - \mu^2)}{r} \frac{\partial \psi_i(r, \mu)}{\partial \mu} + \Sigma_i \psi_i(r, \mu)$$
$$= \int_0^{2\pi} \int_{-1}^{+1} \sum_j \Sigma_{ji}(\mu_0) \psi_i(r, \mu') \, d\mu' \, d\omega, \quad (30)$$

where $\Sigma_{ji}(\mu_0)$ is the transfer cross-section representing the transfer of neutrons from one group j to i which are scattered through an angle $\cos^{-1} \mu_0$, where

$$\mu_0 = \mu\mu' - [1 - \mu^2]^{\frac{1}{2}}[1 - (\mu')^2]^{\frac{1}{2}} \cos \omega.$$

The $\Sigma_{ji}(\mu_0)$ are expanded in Legendre polynomials, as in Chapter 7, equation (73), and the right-hand side of (30) becomes

$$\sum_j \sum_{k=0}^{\infty} \frac{1}{2}(2k + 1)\Sigma_{ji, k} P_k(\mu) \int_{-1}^{+1} P_k(\mu') \psi_j(r, \mu') \, d\mu', \quad (31)$$

where $\qquad \Sigma_{ji, k} = 2\pi \int_{-1}^{+1} P_k(\mu_0) \Sigma_{ji}(\mu_0) \, d\mu_0.$

This series is terminated after a number of terms, say after $k = \mathrm{K}$. The Carlson method is then applied as before, and $\psi(r, \mu)$ is assumed to be a linear function of μ in an angular interval $\mu_{n-1} < \mu < \mu_n$. The right-hand side then becomes a triple sum. The resulting equations are solved as before.

This is a brief outline of the S_n method applied to anisotropic scattering. An account of the method and the machine programmes which are available to solve the resulting set of equations has been given by Ackroyd and Pendlebury [45].

8.4 Multi-group diffusion theory

(a) Two group theory

The one velocity group asymptotic theory was described in Chapter 5. This theory can be extended to take account of two velocity groups. Let ϕ_1, ϕ_2 be the fluxes and Σ_1, Σ_2 the total macroscopic cross-sections in the two groups. Let Σ_{11} and Σ_{12} be the number of secondaries per unit path produced in the first and second group respectively by a neutron in the first group. Σ_{22} and Σ_{21} are similar quantities for the second group. The fluxes ϕ_1 and ϕ_2 satisfy the pair of integral equations

$$\phi_1(\mathbf{r}) = \frac{\Sigma_{11}}{4\pi} \int |\mathbf{r} - \mathbf{r}'|^{-2} \exp\left[-\Sigma_1 |\mathbf{r} - \mathbf{r}'|\right] \phi_1(\mathbf{r}') \, dV'$$
$$+ \frac{\Sigma_{21}}{4\pi} \int |\mathbf{r} - \mathbf{r}'|^{-2} \exp\left[-\Sigma_1 |\mathbf{r} - \mathbf{r}'|\right] \phi_2(\mathbf{r}') \, dV'. \quad (32)$$

$$\phi_2(\mathbf{r}) = \frac{\Sigma_{12}}{4\pi} \int |\mathbf{r} - \mathbf{r}'|^{-2} \exp\left[-\Sigma_2 |\mathbf{r} - \mathbf{r}'|\right] \phi_1(\mathbf{r}') \, dV'$$
$$+ \frac{\Sigma_{22}}{4\pi} \int |\mathbf{r} - \mathbf{r}'|^{-2} \exp\left[-\Sigma_2 |\mathbf{r} - \mathbf{r}'|\right] \phi_2(\mathbf{r}') \, dV'. \quad (33)$$

The asymptotic solution of these equations valid at points distant from sources and boundaries can be obtained by expanding $\phi_1(\mathbf{r}')$ and $\phi_2(\mathbf{r}')$ as Taylor series as in the one-group case (see Chapter 5, equation (3)).

$\phi_1(\mathbf{r}')$ and $\phi_2(\mathbf{r}')$ are given by the following series:

$$\phi_1(\mathbf{r}') = \phi_1(x', y', z') = \phi_1(x, y, z)$$
$$+ (x' - x) \frac{\partial \phi_1}{\partial x} + (y' - y) \frac{\partial \phi_1}{\partial y} + (z' - z) \frac{\partial \phi_1}{\partial z} + \ldots,$$

$$\phi_2(\mathbf{r}') = \phi_2(x', y', z') = \phi_2(x, y, z)$$
$$+ (x' - x) \frac{\partial \phi_2}{\partial x} + (y' - y) \frac{\partial \phi_2}{\partial y} + (z' - z) \frac{\partial \phi_2}{\partial z} + \ldots.$$

These series are then substituted into (32) and (33). Then the following equations are obtained for $\phi_1(\mathbf{r})$ and $\phi_2(\mathbf{r})$:

$$\left. \begin{aligned}
\phi_1(\mathbf{r}) &= \frac{\Sigma_{11}}{\Sigma_1} \left[\phi_1(\mathbf{r}) + \tfrac{1}{3}\Sigma^{-2}\nabla^2\phi_1(\mathbf{r}) + \tfrac{1}{5}\Sigma_1^{-4}\nabla^4\phi_1(\mathbf{r}) \ldots\right] \\
&\quad + \frac{\Sigma_{21}}{\Sigma_1} \left[\phi_2(\mathbf{r}) + \tfrac{1}{3}\Sigma_1^{-2}\nabla^2\phi_2(\mathbf{r}) + \ldots\right] \\
\phi_2(\mathbf{r}) &= \frac{\Sigma_{12}}{\Sigma_2} \left[\phi_1(\mathbf{r}) + \tfrac{1}{3}\Sigma_2^{-2}\nabla^2\phi_1(\mathbf{r}) + \tfrac{1}{5}\Sigma_2^{-4}\nabla^4\phi_1(\mathbf{r}) \ldots\right] \\
&\quad + \frac{\Sigma_{22}}{\Sigma_2} \left[\phi_2(\mathbf{r}) + \tfrac{1}{3}\Sigma_2^{-2}\nabla^2\phi_2(\mathbf{r}) \ldots\right].
\end{aligned} \right\} \quad (34)$$

As in the one-velocity group case let Y be a solution of

$$\nabla^2 Y = \kappa^2 Y.$$

Then $\phi_1(\mathbf{r}) = Y$ and $\phi_2(\mathbf{r}) = \zeta Y$ are solutions of (34) provided that κ and ζ satisfy the relations

$$[\kappa - \Sigma_{11} \tanh^{-1}(\kappa/\Sigma_1)][\kappa - \Sigma_{22} \tanh^{-1}(\kappa/\Sigma_2)]$$
$$= \Sigma_{12}\Sigma_{21} \tanh^{-1}(\kappa/\Sigma_1) \tanh^{-1}(\kappa/\Sigma_2), \quad (35)$$

and $$\zeta = [\kappa \tanh^{-1}(\kappa/\Sigma_1) - \Sigma_{11}]/\Sigma_{21}. \quad (36)$$

The derivation of these equations is valid only if $|\kappa| < \Sigma_1$ and $< \Sigma_2$. Certain combinations of the values of the constants have the result that the roots of (35) do not meet these conditions and the roots are therefore unusable.

When $\Sigma_1 \sim \Sigma_{11}$, $\Sigma_2 \sim \Sigma_{22}$, equation (35) reduces to

$$[\kappa^2 - 3\Sigma_1(\Sigma_{11} - \Sigma_1)][\kappa^2 - 3\Sigma_2(\Sigma_{22} - \Sigma_2)] = 9\Sigma_{12}\Sigma_{21}\Sigma_1\Sigma_2. \quad (37)$$

The current vectors $\mathbf{j}$ and $\mathbf{j}_2$ in the two groups are given by

$$\mathbf{j}_1 = -\tfrac{1}{3}\Sigma_1^{-1} \operatorname{grad} \phi_1 \text{ and } \mathbf{j}_2 = -\tfrac{1}{3}\Sigma_2^{-1} \operatorname{grad} \phi_2. \quad (38)$$

These are the equations of the P_1 approximation in the spherical harmonics method, or simple diffusion theory.

(b) Many energy groups

Let us now consider the form of the P_1 approximation in multi-group theory. The numerical procedures will be illustrated by a critical size calculation for a spherically symmetrical system. The flux is then a function of only one spatial co-ordinate, the distance of a point from the centre of the system.

Let ϕ_i be the neutron flux in a particular group i. Then ϕ_i satisfies the equation

$$-\tfrac{1}{3}\Sigma_i^{-1} \frac{d^2(r\phi_i)}{dr^2} + r\Sigma_i\phi_i = r \sum_j \Sigma'_{ji}\phi_j + rg_i, \quad (39)$$

where Σ_i is the macroscopic cross-section. Σ'_{ji} is the appropriate cross-section per unit volume for transfer from group j to group i by processes other than fission (Σ'_{jj} being the corresponding cross-section for neutrons to remain in group j after scattering). g_i is the number of fission neutrons in group i, i.e.

$$g_i = G_i \sum_j \phi_j \Sigma_{jf}, \quad (40)$$

where Σ_{jf} is the cross-section per unit volume for fission in group j, and G_i is the fraction of fission neutrons emitted in group i. In principle, an analytic solution of equations (39) can be written down for a system consisting of a core and any number of layers of reflector. However, when the number of groups is large the resulting expressions become very complicated from an algebraic point of view and a numerical procedure is preferable.

Equations (39) are solved by a source iteration technique: one assumes a given distribution of fissions, determines the fluxes in each group, and then calculates a new fission source distribution g_i. The iteration procedure is different from that used in the Carlson method. In the latter, one starts with guesses of the fluxes in different groups and from these the angular distributions of flux are calculated.

The fission source iteration process is repeated until the ratio of $g_i(r)$ for two consecutive iterations is independent of r and equal to m, which is the multiplication rate per generation of neutrons. For a critical system m is unity. The actual value of a critical parameter, say the core radius, can be obtained by carrying out the calculation for several values of the radius, and the value for which m is unity is found by interpolation.

Mandl [46] obtained the equations (39) by considering the P_1 approximation of the multi-group version of the spherical harmonics form of the Boltzmann equation. Ehrlich and Hurwitz [47] have shown how the equations (39) can be obtained from the age equation, which is an approximation to the transport equation. The integration of the age equation has been considered by Howlett and Mandl also [48]. In these numerical procedures the range of integration over r is divided into equal intervals Δr in the core, and equal (but possibly different from Δr) intervals in the reflector. Let the space points be denoted by r_m and let

$$r_m \phi_i(r_m) = \phi_{im}.$$

Then
$$\frac{d^2[r\phi_i(r)]}{dr^2} = \frac{\phi_{i,\,m+1} + \phi_{i,\,m-1} - 2\phi_{i,\,m}}{(\Delta r)^2}. \tag{41}$$

On substituting into equation (39), one obtains an equation

$$\phi_{i,\,m+1} = k_i \phi_{i,\,m} - \phi_{i,\,m-1} - I_{im}, \tag{42}$$

where
$$k_i = 2 + 3\Sigma_i(\Sigma_i - \Sigma'_{ii})(\Delta r)^2,$$

and
$$I_{im} = 3\Sigma_i(\Delta r)^2 \sum_{j \neq i} \Sigma'_{ji}\phi_{jm} + 3r_m \Sigma_i g_{im}(\Delta r)^2.$$

121

The flux will decrease in the reflector, and in the solution of (39) errors may appear which increase for increasing r_m. There are several techniques which are available to avoid this difficulty and these are discussed by Ehrlich and Hurwitz.

In the integration of the age equation other instabilities may arise depending on the particular process which is used. The age equation was derived in Chapter 7. Howlett and Mandl considered the equation for the collision density $F_0(u, r) = E\Sigma\phi(E, r)$, i.e.

$$-\tfrac{1}{3}\Sigma^{-2}\frac{\partial^2(rF_0)}{\partial r^2} + \xi\,\frac{\partial(rF_0)}{\partial u} + p_c rF_0 = rg(r)\delta(u), \qquad (43)$$

where u is the lethargy, p_c is the probability of capture per collision and $g(r)$ is the source term of fission neutrons, which are assumed to be emitted with an energy corresponding to zero lethargy. They took intervals u' in lethargy, and intervals Δr in r. Let

$$u_i = iu',\ r_m = m\Delta r \text{ and } \chi = rF_0.$$

Using the approximations

$$\left[\frac{\partial\chi}{\partial u}\right]_{i,\,m} = (u')^{-1}[\chi_{i+1,\,m} - \chi_{i,\,m}]. \qquad (44)$$

$$\left[\frac{\partial^2\chi}{\partial r^2}\right]_{i,\,m} = (\Delta r)^{-2}[\chi_{i,\,m+1} - 2\chi_{i,\,m} + \chi_{i,\,m-1}]. \qquad (45)$$

Then equation (43) becomes for $i > 0$:

$$\chi_{i+1,\,m} = \frac{u'}{(\Delta r 3\xi\Sigma^2)}\,[\chi_{i,\,m+1} - \{2 - 3(u')^{-1}(\Delta r)^2(\xi - u'p_c)\Sigma^2\}\chi_{i,\,m} + \chi_{i,\,m-1}]. \qquad (46)$$

By taking the forward difference for $\partial r/\partial u$ in formula (44) it is then possible to calculate $\chi_{i+1,\,m}$ from the $\chi_{i,\,m}$'s in (46). If an alternative formula for $\partial\chi/\partial u$ had been taken, i.e.

$$(\partial\chi/\partial u)_{j,\,m} = (1/u')[\chi_{i,\,m} - \chi_{i-1,\,m}], \qquad (47)$$

then equations of the form (42) would have been obtained. The equations (46) can be solved by an iteration technique. The values at $i = 0$ are determined by the assumed fission distribution $g(r)$. All the χ_i are then calculated and a new fission distribution is determined. However, this scheme is only stable numerically if

$$u' < (\Delta r)^2$$

i.e. a large number of lethargy intervals must be taken. However, the iteration procedure is a stable process for the solution of equations (42) irrespective of the values of the width of the energy groups compared with Δr.

8.5 Perturbation theory

In some problems one wishes to determine the change in the reactivity of a critical system due to small changes in either the material composition or the geometry of a system. The change in reactivity can be calculated using perturbation theory. Accounts of perturbation theory have been given by various authors, including Fuchs [49], Glasstone and Edlund [50], Tait [51] and Pendlebury [52]. Fuchs considered the one-group integral equation; Glasstone and Edlund describe multi-group theory starting from the diffusion equation; Tait dealt with the two group integral equations, and Pendlebury started from the transport equation and his analysis is the most general.

(a) Perturbation theory of the transport equation

Pendlebury considers Chapter 2, equation (16), which was obtained from the time dependent transport equation, Chapter 2, equation (4), by the substitution

$$N(\mathbf{r}, v, \mathbf{\Omega}, t) = \exp(\alpha t)N(\mathbf{r}, v, \mathbf{\Omega}).$$

The transport equation is

$$v\mathbf{\Omega} \cdot \text{grad } N(\mathbf{r}, v, \mathbf{\Omega}) + (\alpha + \Sigma v)N(\mathbf{r}, v, \mathbf{\Omega}) =$$
$$\iint v'c(v')\Sigma(v')f(v', \mathbf{\Omega}' \longrightarrow v, \mathbf{\Omega})N(\mathbf{r}, v', \mathbf{\Omega}') \, dv' \, d\Omega'. \quad (48)$$

In order to eliminate variations δN in the neutron density when this equation is perturbed, the adjoint equation, Chapter 2, equation (18) is also considered, i.e.

$$-v\mathbf{\Omega} \cdot \text{grad } N^\dagger(\mathbf{r}, v, \mathbf{\Omega}) + (\alpha_1 + \Sigma_1 v)N^\dagger(\mathbf{r}, v, \mathbf{\Omega})$$
$$= \iint vc_1(v)\Sigma_1(v)f(v, \mathbf{\Omega} \longrightarrow v', \mathbf{\Omega}')N^\dagger(\mathbf{r}, v', \mathbf{\Omega}') \, dv' \, d\Omega'. \quad (49)$$

In the equation (49) the quantities Σ, c and α have a subscript 1. Multiply equation (48) by $N^\dagger(\mathbf{r}, v, \mathbf{\Omega})$ and (49) by $N(\mathbf{r}, v, \mathbf{\Omega})$, subtract the two equations and integrate over all velocities, directions and space. The following equation is obtained:

$$\iiint v\boldsymbol{\Omega} \cdot \text{grad} \, [N(\mathbf{r}, v, \boldsymbol{\Omega})N^\dagger(\mathbf{r}, v, \boldsymbol{\Omega})] \, dv \, d\Omega \, dV +$$

$$(\alpha - \alpha_1) \iiint N(\mathbf{r}, v, \boldsymbol{\Omega})N^\dagger(\mathbf{r}, v, \boldsymbol{\Omega}) \, dv \, d\Omega \, dV$$

$$= - \iiint (\Sigma - \Sigma_1) \, vN(\mathbf{r}, v, \boldsymbol{\Omega})N^\dagger(\mathbf{r}, v, \boldsymbol{\Omega}) \, dv \, d\Omega \, dV$$

$$+ \iiiint\!\!\int v'[c(v')\Sigma(v') - c_1(v')\Sigma_1(v')]f(v', \boldsymbol{\Omega}' \longrightarrow v, \boldsymbol{\Omega})$$

$$N(\mathbf{r}, v', \boldsymbol{\Omega}')N^\dagger(\mathbf{r}, v, \boldsymbol{\Omega}) \, dv \, dv' \, d\Omega \, d\Omega' \, dV. \quad (50)$$

The last integral on the right-hand side of (50) is obtained by first interchanging v, $\boldsymbol{\Omega}$ and v', $\boldsymbol{\Omega}'$ in (49). The integration over the volume V in the first term on the left-hand side of equation (50) can be replaced by an integral over a surface S which encloses the volume V, i.e.

$$\int_V \boldsymbol{\Omega} \, \text{grad} \, [N(\mathbf{r}, v, \boldsymbol{\Omega})N^\dagger(\mathbf{r}, v, \boldsymbol{\Omega})] \, dV = \int N(\mathbf{r}, v, \boldsymbol{\Omega})N^\dagger(\mathbf{r}, v, \boldsymbol{\Omega})\boldsymbol{\Omega} \cdot d\mathbf{S}.$$

Now $N(\mathbf{r}, v, \boldsymbol{\Omega})$ is zero for incoming direction to S and $N^\dagger(\mathbf{r}, v, \boldsymbol{\Omega})$ is zero for outgoing directions. Therefore, the first term on the left-hand side of (50) vanishes. If $(\Sigma - \Sigma_1)$ and $(c\Sigma - c_1\Sigma_1)$ are small then neglecting second-order contributions, the adjoint density $N^\dagger$ can be calculated assuming that $\Sigma = \Sigma_1$ and $c = c_1$ in (49).

Let $\delta\alpha = \alpha - \alpha$, $\delta\Sigma = \Sigma - \Sigma_1$ and $\delta(c\Sigma) = c\Sigma - c_1\Sigma_1$.

Then

$$\delta\alpha \iiint N(\mathbf{r}, v, \boldsymbol{\Omega})N^\dagger(\mathbf{r}, v, \boldsymbol{\Omega}) \, dv \, d\Omega \, dV$$

$$= - \iiint \delta\Sigma(v)vN(\mathbf{r}, v, \boldsymbol{\Omega})N^\dagger(\mathbf{r}, v, \boldsymbol{\Omega}) \, dv \, d\Omega \, dV$$

$$+ \iiiint\!\!\int v'\delta[c(v')\Sigma(v')]f(v', \boldsymbol{\Omega}' \longrightarrow v, \boldsymbol{\Omega})$$

$$N(\mathbf{r}, v', \boldsymbol{\Omega}')N^\dagger(\mathbf{r}, v, \boldsymbol{\Omega}) \, dv \, dv' \, d\Omega \, d\Omega' \, dV. \quad (51)$$

It should be noted that perturbation theory and the variational method (Appendix B) are identical, if one takes the trial function in the variational method to be the solution of (48).

(b) *One group perturbation theory*
In the case of one group theory

$$N(\mathbf{r}, v, \boldsymbol{\Omega}) = \delta(v - v_0)N(\mathbf{r}, \boldsymbol{\Omega}),$$

and

$$N^\dagger(\mathbf{r}, v, \boldsymbol{\Omega}) = \delta(v - v_0)N^\dagger(\mathbf{r}, \boldsymbol{\Omega}).$$

From (49) and (48) it can be seen that

$$N^\dagger(\mathbf{r}, \boldsymbol{\Omega}) = N(\mathbf{r}, -\boldsymbol{\Omega}).$$

For the case of isotropic scattering

$$f(v', \boldsymbol{\Omega}' \longrightarrow v, \boldsymbol{\Omega}) = 1/(4\pi).$$

Let
$$N_0(\mathbf{r}) = \int N(\mathbf{r}, \boldsymbol{\Omega}) \, d\Omega,$$

and
$$W(\mathbf{r}) = [4\pi/N_0{}^2(\mathbf{r})] \int N(\mathbf{r}, \boldsymbol{\Omega}) N(\mathbf{r}, -\boldsymbol{\Omega}) \, d\Omega.$$

Substituting into (51) the following equation is obtained for $\delta\alpha$:

$$(\delta\alpha/v_0)\int W(\mathbf{r})N_0{}^2(\mathbf{r}) \, dV = \int [\delta\{c(r)\Sigma(r)\} - W(\mathbf{r})\delta\Sigma(\mathbf{r})]N_0{}^2(\mathbf{r}) \, dV. \quad (52)$$

(c) Multi-group perturbation theory for the case of isotropic scattering

Formula (9) gives the form of the expressions for the flux in multi-energy group theory. In multi-velocity group theory the expressions are similar

$$vN(\mathbf{r}, v, \boldsymbol{\Omega}) = \sum_i \psi_i(\mathbf{r}, \boldsymbol{\Omega})B_i(v), \quad (53)$$

where $B_i(v)$ is zero for $v \geqslant v_i$ and $v_{i-1} \geqslant v$.

The average values of $\Sigma(v)$ and $c(v)\Sigma(v)$ in a group are defined as follows:

$$\Sigma_i b_i = \int_{v_{i-1}}^{v_i} \Sigma(v)B(v) \, dv,$$

and
$$c_i\Sigma_i b_i = \int_{v_{i-1}}^{v_i} c(v)\Sigma(v)B(v) \, dv,$$

where
$$b_i = \int_{v_{i-1}}^{v_i} B(v) \, dv.$$

(53) gives the form of the expression for the flux. It is assumed that the adjoint density $N^\dagger(\mathbf{r}, v, \boldsymbol{\Omega})$ is given as follows:

$$N^\dagger(\mathbf{r}, v, \boldsymbol{\Omega}) = \sum_i N_i{}^\dagger(\mathbf{r}, \boldsymbol{\Omega}) \, d_i, \quad (54)$$

where d_i is zero for $v \geqslant v_i$ and $v_{i-1} \geqslant v$, and is constant for

$v_i \geqslant v \geqslant v_{i-1}$. Substituting from (53) and (54) into (51) the following formula is obtained for $\delta\alpha$:

$$\delta\alpha \iint \sum_i \psi_i(\mathbf{r}, \mathbf{\Omega}) N_i^\dagger(\mathbf{r}, \mathbf{\Omega}) b_i d_i \, d\Omega dV$$

$$= \iint \sum_i \delta\Sigma_i(\mathbf{r}) \psi_i(\mathbf{r}, \mathbf{\Omega}) N_i^\dagger(\mathbf{r}, \mathbf{\Omega}) b_i d_i \, d\Omega \, dV$$

$$+ \left(\frac{1}{4\pi}\right) \sum_i \sum_j \int \delta(c\Sigma)_i f_{i \longrightarrow j} \phi_i(\mathbf{r}) n_j^\dagger(\mathbf{r}) b_i d_j \, dV, \quad (55)$$

where $\qquad \phi_i(\mathbf{r}) = \int \psi_i(\mathbf{r}, \mathbf{\Omega}) \, d\Omega,$

$$n_i^\dagger(\mathbf{r}) = \int N_i^\dagger(\mathbf{r}, \mathbf{\Omega}) \, d\Omega,$$

and $\;\; b_i \delta(c\Sigma)_i f_{i \longrightarrow j} = \displaystyle\int_{v_{j-1}}^{v_j} \int_{v'_{i-1}}^{v'_i} f(v' \longrightarrow v) \delta[c\Sigma(v')] B_i(v') \, dv \, dv'.$

(d) Perturbation theory in the P_1 approximation

In the P_1 approximation the angular distribution of density for the one velocity group case is given by

$$N(\mathbf{r}, \mathbf{\Omega}) = \left(\frac{1}{4\pi}\right)[N_0(\mathbf{r}) - l\mu \operatorname{grad} N_0(\mathbf{r})]. \quad (56)$$

The function $W(\mathbf{r})$ in (52) is given by

$$\tfrac{1}{2}[N_0(\mathbf{r})]^{-2} \int [N_0^2(\mathbf{r}) - l^2\mu^2\{\operatorname{grad} N_0(\mathbf{r})\}^2] \, d\mu.$$

Substituting into (52) the following formula is obtained for $\delta\alpha$:

$$(\delta\alpha/v_0)\int [N_0^2(\mathbf{r}) - \tfrac{1}{3}l^2\{\operatorname{grad} N_0(\mathbf{r})\}^2] \, dV$$

$$= \int (\delta[\{c - 1\}\Sigma]N_0^2(\mathbf{r}) + \tfrac{1}{3}\delta\Sigma l^2[\operatorname{grad} N_0(\mathbf{r})]^2) \, dV. \quad (57)$$

From this formula it can be seen that the change in $\Sigma(c - 1)$, which is the capture probability per unit path, is weighted by the square of the density. The change in the mean free path $l^2\delta\Sigma$ is weighted by the square of the gradient of the density.

8.6 Group constants

There is not a universally accepted set of constants for use in a given type of calculation. This is partly due to the mathematical approximations and partly due to the lack of fundamental cross-sectional data. For example, a group may have been chosen which spans a large energy range where the cross-section may have a resonance structure. The group constants can only be determined from first principles if the resonances have been resolved experimentally and if the spectrum can be calculated in the group. When the fundamental data are lacking, group constants can be determined empirically to reproduce the value of some integral quantity which has been determined experimentally.

Parker [53] has given a list of references of group constants which are available. Okrent [54] has given constants which can be used in fast reactor calculations.

APPENDIX A

Relation between the velocity, energy and lethargy scales

It is sometimes convenient to consider various quantities, e.g. the neutron density as either a function of velocity, energy or lethargy. The choice of a particular scale depends on the problem which is being considered.

If the neutron mass is taken as unity then the neutron energy $E = \frac{1}{2}v^2$. The neutron lethargy is defined as $2 \ln (v_0/v)$, where v_0 is some arbitrary velocity.

Then
$$dE = v \, dv, \tag{1}$$

and
$$du = -2 \, dv/v. \tag{2}$$

Let us now consider various quantities as a function of the neutron velocity, energy or lethargy.

(i) *Neutron density*

Let an interval be denoted by dv, dE and du on the velocity, energy and lethargy scales respectively. Let the number of neutrons in this interval be given by $N_1(v) \, dv$, $N_2(E) \, dE$ and $N_3(u) \, du$ on the three scales respectively.

From
$$N_1(v) \, dv = N_2(E) \, dE \text{ and (1) it follows that}$$
$$N_1(v) = vN_2(E),$$

and from
$$N_1(v) \, dv = N_3(u) \, du \text{ and (2) we obtain}$$
$$N_1(v) = -(2/v) \, N_3(u).$$

(ii) *Probability of scattering from one velocity to another*

Let $f_1(v' \longrightarrow v) \, dv$ be the probability of scattering from the neutron velocity v' to the velocity interval dv, $f_2(E' \longrightarrow E) \, dE$ the probability of scattering from an energy E' to the energy interval dE and $f_3(u' \longrightarrow u) \, du$ the probability of scattering from a lethargy u' to a lethargy interval du.

The number scattered to an interval is the same whether or not it is measured on the velocity, energy or lethargy scales.

Therefore
$$f_1(v' \longrightarrow v) \, dv = f_2(E' \longrightarrow E) \, dE, \text{ and}$$

using (1) we find that

$$f_1(v' \longrightarrow v) = v f_2(E' \longrightarrow E).$$

One can also show that

$$f_1(v' \longrightarrow v) = -(2/v) f_3(u' \longrightarrow u).$$

(iii) *Group constants*

The solution of the transport equation is sometimes obtained by dividing the velocity or energy ranges into intervals. The cross-sections are then averaged over these intervals. Consider a typical velocity interval $[v_{i-1}, v_i]$ which corresponds to an energy interval $[E_{i-1} E_i]$. Let $B_1(v)$ be the spectrum in the velocity group $[v_{i-1}, v_i]$ and $B_2(E)$ that in the energy group, $[E_{i-1}, E_i]$. Then $v B_2(E) = B_1(v)$. Let $\Sigma_{i, 1}$ be the average value of a cross-section $\Sigma(v)$ over $[v_{i-1}. v_i]$, (the subscript 1 denotes velocity averages and the subscript 2 energy average),

i.e.
$$b_{i, 1} \Sigma_{i, 1} = \int_{v_{i-1}}^{v_i} B_1(v) \, \Sigma(v) \, dv,$$

where
$$b_{i, 1} = \int_{v_{i-1}}^{v_i} B_1(v) \, dv.$$

On the energy scale the average value $\Sigma_{i, 2}$ is given by

$$b_{i, 2} \Sigma_{i, 2} = \int_{E_{i-1}}^{E_i} B_2(E) \Sigma(E) \, dE,$$

where
$$b_{i, 2} = \int_{E_{i-1}}^{E_i} B_2(E) \, dE.$$

Now
$$b_{i, 1} = \int_{v_{i-1}}^{v_i} v B_2(E) \, dv = b_{i, 2},$$

and
$$b_{i, 1} \Sigma_{i, 1} = \int_{v_{i-1}}^{v_i} v \, B_2(E) \Sigma(v) \, dv,$$

$$= b_{i, 2} \Sigma_{i, 2},$$

i.e.
$$\Sigma_{i, 1} = \Sigma_{i, 2}$$

which is a result one would have expected on physical arguments.

Appendix A

It can be shown similarly that the cross-section $\Sigma_{j\rightarrow i,\,1}$ for the transfer from the velocity group $[v_{j-1}, v_j]$ to $[v_{i-1}, v_i]$ is the same as that for the transfer from the groups defined on the energy scale, where $\Sigma_{j\rightarrow i,\,1}$ is defined as follows:

$$b_{j,\,1} \Sigma_{j\rightarrow i,\,1} = \int_{v_{i-1}}^{v_i} \int_{v'_{j-1}}^{v'_j} B_1(v') f_1(v' \longrightarrow v) \Sigma(v')\, dv'\, dv.$$

APPENDIX B

Variational Method

The application of the variational method to problems in neutron transport theory has been discussed by Selengut [24] and Rowlands [55]. In this Appendix the application of the method is not discussed in great detail, and the discussion is restricted to a few applications of the method. Selengut and Rowlands found it convenient to use the notation of linear operator theory and this has been used in the following.

Let the equation describing a given system be written

$$L\phi(x) = S(x), \tag{1}$$

where L is a linear operator, $\phi(x)$ is the flux and $S(x)$ is a source term. In the case of one velocity group integral equation, Chapter 3, equation (31), $L\phi(x)$ is given as follows:

$$\int_0^\infty [\delta(x - x') - \tfrac{1}{2}\Sigma E_1(\Sigma \, | \, x - x' \, |)]\phi(x') \, dx',$$

where $\delta(x - x')$ is Dirac's δ function as defined previously.

Adjoint operator

The following equation is considered also with (1)

$$L^\dagger \phi^\dagger(x) = S^\dagger(x), \tag{2}$$

where $L^\dagger$ is the adjoint operator. It has the following property

$$\int v(x)L^\dagger u(x) \, dx = \int u(x)Lv(x) \, dx. \tag{3}$$

If L does not contain any differential operators then $u(x)$ and $v(x)$ can be any two functions. However, if L does contain differential operators and ϕ is obtained by solving (1) with the appropriate boundary conditions, then the functions $u(x)$ and $v(x)$ must satisfy the same boundary conditions as $\phi(x)$ and $\phi^\dagger(x)$ respectively.

Functional $J(\phi, \phi^\dagger)$

Let J denote the following functional

$$J = (S^\dagger \phi) + (S\phi^\dagger) - (\phi^\dagger, L\phi), \tag{4}$$

131

where
$$(S^\dagger \phi) = \int S^\dagger(x)\phi(x)\, dx, \tag{5}$$

$$(S\phi^\dagger) = \int S(x)\phi^\dagger(x)\, dx, \tag{6}$$

and
$$(\phi^\dagger, L\phi) = \int \phi^\dagger(x)L\phi(x)\, dx = \int \phi(x)L^\dagger\phi^\dagger(x)\, dx,$$
$$= (\phi, L^\dagger\phi^\dagger). \tag{7}$$

For exact values of ϕ and $\phi^\dagger$ (4) reduces to:

$$J = (S^\dagger\phi) = (S\phi^\dagger). \tag{8}$$

Let
$$\phi(x) = \phi_0(x) + \varepsilon(x), \tag{9}$$

and
$$\phi^\dagger(x) = \phi_0^\dagger(x) + \varepsilon^\dagger(x), \tag{10}$$

where $\phi_0(x)$ and $\phi_0^\dagger(x)$ are approximations to $\phi(x)$ and $\phi^\dagger(x)$ with errors $\varepsilon(x)$ and $\varepsilon^\dagger(x)$ respectively. Substitute into (4) one obtains, after some algebraic manipulation using (3), the following result:

$$J = J_0 + (\varepsilon^\dagger, L\varepsilon), \tag{11}$$

where
$$J_0 = (S^\dagger\phi_0) + (S\phi_0^\dagger) - (\phi_0^\dagger, L\phi_0). \tag{12}$$

ϕ_0 and $\phi_0^\dagger$ are considered as approximations to ϕ and $\phi^\dagger$ and have first order errors. However, the error in J is of second order.‡ This property can be used as follows. Interpreting ε as $\delta\phi$ and $\varepsilon^\dagger$ as $\delta\phi^\dagger$, then from (11)

$$\delta J/\delta\phi = 0, \text{ as } \varepsilon^\dagger \longrightarrow 0,$$
and
$$\delta J/\delta\phi^\dagger = 0, \text{ as } \varepsilon \longrightarrow 0,$$

i.e. J is an extremum with respect to arbitrary variations in ϕ_0 and $\phi_0^\dagger$.

Alternative functional

The functional J as given by (4) depends on the amplitudes of ϕ and $\phi^\dagger$. A functional which does not depend on the amplitudes can be obtained in the following way:

Let
$$\phi = C_1\phi_1 \text{ and } \phi^\dagger = C_1^\dagger\phi_1^\dagger, \tag{13}$$

where C_1 and $C_1^\dagger$ are constants.

---

‡ An example of the errors in J as a function of those in ϕ_0 is given on p. 38. The error in the trial function is 3.10^{-3}, but the error in the quantity calculated by the variational method is 4.10^{-7}.

Appendix B

The change $\delta\phi$ in ϕ and $\delta\phi^\dagger$ in $\phi^\dagger$ is considered in two stages:

    (i) a certain variation with respect to C_1 and $C_1^\dagger$,
    (ii) an arbitrary variation of ϕ_1 and $\phi_1^\dagger$.

Let C_1 and $C_1^\dagger$ be changed by amounts δC_1 and $\delta C_1^\dagger$ respectively. Then the change in J is given by

$$\delta J = \delta C_1(S^\dagger\phi_1) + \delta C_1^\dagger(S\phi_1^\dagger) - [C_1\delta C_1^\dagger + C_1^\dagger\delta C_1](\phi_1^\dagger, L\phi_1).$$

If J is an extremum for arbitrary variations in C_1 and $C_1^\dagger$, then

$$C_1 = \frac{(S\phi_1^\dagger)}{(\phi_1^\dagger, L\phi_1)} \text{ and } C_1^\dagger = \frac{(S^\dagger\phi_1)}{(\phi_1^\dagger, L\phi_1)}. \tag{14}$$

Substituting into (4) results in a value of J given by

$$J = J_1 = \frac{(S\phi_1^\dagger)(S^\dagger\phi_1)}{(\phi_1^\dagger, L\phi_1)}. \tag{15}$$

Variations in ϕ_1 and $\phi_1^\dagger$ are considered now, i.e.

$$C_1\phi_1 = \phi = \phi_0 + \varepsilon,$$
$$C_1\phi_1^\dagger = \phi^\dagger = \phi_0^\dagger + \varepsilon^\dagger.$$

Now
$$J_1 = \frac{(S\phi^\dagger)(S^\dagger\phi)}{(\phi^\dagger, L\phi)},$$
$$= (S\phi^\dagger),$$

as $\quad (\phi^\dagger, L\phi) = (\phi, L^\dagger\phi^\dagger) = (S^\dagger\phi)$ for the exact ϕ and $\phi^\dagger$.

Therefore
$$J_1 = (S\phi_0^\dagger) + (S\varepsilon^\dagger),$$
$$= (S\phi_0^\dagger) + (\varepsilon^\dagger, L\phi_0) + (\varepsilon^\dagger, L\varepsilon).$$

Then $\quad J_1 - \dfrac{(S\phi_0^\dagger)(S^\dagger\phi_0)}{(\phi_0^\dagger, L\phi_0)} = (\varepsilon^\dagger, L\varepsilon)$

$$+ \frac{(S\phi_0^\dagger)[(\phi_0^\dagger, L\phi_0) - (S^\dagger\phi_0)] + (\varepsilon^\dagger, L\phi_0)(\phi_0^\dagger, L\phi_0)}{(\phi_0^\dagger, L\phi_0)}. \tag{16}$$

After some manipulation it can be shown that the second term on the right-hand side of (16) is equal to

$$- \frac{(\varepsilon^\dagger, L\phi_0)(\phi_0^\dagger, L\varepsilon)}{(\phi_0^\dagger, L\phi_0)},$$

using (1), (2) and (3).

133

Thus an estimate of J is given by

$$\frac{(S\phi_0)(S^\dagger\phi_0)}{(\phi_0^\dagger, L\phi_0)}. \tag{17}$$

This does not depend on the magnitude of $\phi_0^\dagger$ and ϕ_0.

One group theory

In one velocity group theory the neutron flux $\phi(x)$ satisfies an equation of the type

$$\phi(x) = \int \phi(x')K(x', x)\,dx' + S(x), \tag{18}$$

i.e. $\qquad L\phi(x) = \int [\delta(x - x') - K(x', x)]\phi(x')\,dx'.$

If $K(x', x)$ is symmetrical in x and x', then the adjoint operator $L^\dagger$ is identical to L, it is easily seen that

$$\int uLv\,dx = \int vLu\,dx.$$

If $S^\dagger(x) = S(x)$, then $\phi^\dagger(x) = \phi(x)$.

The kernel $K(x', x)$ of equation (18) is sometimes of the form $c(x')\Sigma(x')k(x', x)$, where $k(x', x)$ is a symmetrical function in x and x'. In this case the adjoint operator is given as follows:

$$L^\dagger\phi^\dagger(x) = \int [\delta(x - x') - c(x)\Sigma(x)k(x', x)]\phi^\dagger(x')\,dx'.$$

If $S^\dagger(x) = c(x)\Sigma(x)S(x)$ then it can be shown that the solution of the adjoint equation $\phi^\dagger(x)$ is equal to $c(x)\Sigma(x)\phi(x)$.

When $K(x, x')$ is symmetrical and $S^\dagger(x) = S(x)$ the functional $J(\phi_0)$ given by (12) has the following form:

$$2(S\phi_0) - (\phi_0, L\phi_0), \tag{19}$$

and (17) becomes

$$\frac{(S\phi_0)^2}{(\phi_0, L\phi_0)}. \tag{20}$$

When $K(x', x) = c(x')\Sigma(x')k(x', x)$,

then $\qquad J(\phi_0) = 2(Sc\Sigma\phi_0) - (c\Sigma\phi_0, L\phi_0), \tag{21}$

and (17) is given as follows:

$$\frac{(Sc\Sigma\phi_0)^2}{(c\Sigma\phi_0, L\phi_0)}.$$ (22)

When $S = 0$, the one velocity homogeneous equation is soluble for certain values of α, where α is introduced in the equation as follows:

$$\phi(x) = \alpha \int K(x', x)\phi(x')\, dx'.$$

The functional $J(\phi) = 0$. Therefore, for a trial function $\phi = \phi_0$,

$$J(\phi_0) = (\phi_0, L\phi_0) = 0,$$

i.e.
$$\alpha^{-1} = \frac{\int \phi_0(x) \int K(x', x)\phi_0(x')\, dx'\, dx}{\int [\phi_0(x)]^2\, dx}.$$ (23)

This gives the value of the lower eigenvalue.

Alternative use of the functional $J(\phi, \phi^\dagger)$

An alternative use of the functional $J(\phi, \phi^\dagger)$ is to assume that it is stationary for small variations $\delta\phi$, $\delta\phi^\dagger$ in ϕ and $\phi^\dagger$ respectively, and then deduce equations for ϕ and $\phi^\dagger$.

Now
$$J = (S^\dagger\phi) + (S\phi^\dagger) - (\phi^\dagger, L\phi),$$

and for small variations of $\delta\phi$ and $\delta\phi^\dagger$ in ϕ and $\phi^\dagger$,

$$J = (\delta\phi^\dagger, S - L\phi) + (\delta\phi, S^\dagger - L^\dagger\phi^\dagger).$$ (24)

For arbitrary $\delta\phi$ and $\delta\phi^\dagger$ the condition $J = 0$ leads to the equations

$$L\phi = S,$$
$$L^\dagger\phi^\dagger = S^\dagger.$$

The above is exact. In an approximate method ϕ and $\phi^\dagger$ are expressed in terms of a set of functions ϕ_n and $\phi_n{}^\dagger$, and equations are derived by the variation of these functions. An example is given in Chapter 5, Section 5.6.

ϕ and $\phi^\dagger$ have been considered as functions of one variable x. The above analysis can be shown to be valid when they are functions of a multidimensional variable $\mathbf{x}$.

APPENDIX C

Optical Reciprocity Theorem

Let $\phi(x_1 \longrightarrow x)$ be the flux at x due to an isotropic source at x_1. Then the optical reciprocity theorem states that

$$\phi(x_1 \longrightarrow x) = \phi(x \longrightarrow x_1). \tag{1}$$

This can be proved for the case of isotropic scattering as follows:

$\phi(x_1 \longrightarrow x)$ satisfies the following equation:

$$\phi(x_1 \longrightarrow x) = \tfrac{1}{2}\int \phi(x_1 \longrightarrow x')c(x')\Sigma(x')E_1(\Sigma \,|\, x - x' \,|)\, dx' \\ + \tfrac{1}{2}E_1(\Sigma \,|\, x - x_1 \,|), \tag{2}$$

where the source strength is unity.

Equation (2) can be rewritten as follows:

$$\phi(x_1 \longrightarrow x) = \tfrac{1}{2}\int \phi(x_1' \longrightarrow x)c(x_1')\Sigma(x_1')E_1(\Sigma \,|\, x_1' - x_1 \,|)\, dx_1' \\ + \tfrac{1}{2}E_1(\Sigma \,|\, x - x_1 \,|). \tag{3}$$

In (3) $\phi(x_1' \longrightarrow x)$ is the flux at x due to unit source at x_1', $\tfrac{1}{2}E_1(\Sigma \,|\, x_1' - x_1 \,|)$ is the flux at x_1' due to the sources at x_1 and $\tfrac{1}{2}c(x_1')\Sigma(x_1')E_1(\Sigma \,|\, x_1' - x_1 \,|)$ neutrons are produced by this flux at x_1'.

If x_1 and x are interchanged in (3) and x_1' is replaced by x', then it can be seen that $\phi(x \longrightarrow x_1)$ and $\phi(x_1 \longrightarrow x)$ satisfy the same equation.

BIBLIOGRAPHY

1. DAVISON, B. (1957). *Neutron Transport Theory*. Oxford University Press.
2. BREIT, G., and WIGNER, E. P. (1936). *Phys. Rev.* **49**, 519.
3. EGELSTAFF, P. A., and SCHOFIELD, P. (1962). *Nuclear Science and Engineering*, **12**, No. 2.
4. WEINBERG, A. M., and WIGNER, E. P. (1958). *The Physical Theory of Neutron Chain Reactors*. The University of Chicago Press.
5. CRANBERG, L., FRYE, G., NERESON, N., and ROSEN, L. (1956). *Phys. Rev.*, **103**, 662.
6. BETHE, H. A., and PLACZEK, G. (1937). *Phys. Rev.*, **51**, 450.
7. HINMAN, G. W., and SAMPSON, J. B. (1962). *General Atomics Report*, 3603.
8. MARSHAK, R. (1947). *Rev. Mod. Phys.*, **19**, No. 3.
9. HOPF, E. (1933). *Mathematical Problems of Radiative Equilibrium, Cambridge Tracts*, No. 31.
10. LECAINE, J. (1947). *Phys. Rev.*, **72**, 564.
11. LECAINE, J. (1950). *Canad. J. Res.*, A, **28**, 242.
12. CASE, K. M., HOFFMANN, F. DE, and PLACZEK, G. (1953). *Introduction to the Theory of Neutron Diffusion*. U.S. Government Printing Office.
13. JAHNKE, E., and EMDE, F. (1944). *Tables of Functions*. Dover Publications.
14. MARK, J. C. (1944). National Research Council of Canada, Atomic Energy Project, Report M.T. 92.
15. YVON, J. (1957). *J. Nuclear Energy*, **4**, 305.
16. ASPELUND, O. (1958). *Proceedings of the Second International Conference on the Peaceful Uses of Atomic Energy*. Geneva Paper 573.
17. CHANDRASEKHAR, S. (1950). *Radiative Transfer*. Oxford University Press.
18. WICK, G. C. (1943). *Z. Phys.*, **121**, 702.
19. GOERTZEL, G. (1958). *Nuclear Science and Engineering*, **4**, 581.
20. CARTER, C., and ROWLANDS, G. (1961). *Journal of Nuclear Energy*, **15**, 1.
21. MARSHAK, R. E. (1947). *Phys. Rev.*, **71**, 443.
22. DAVISON, B. (1951). *Proc. Phys. Soc.*, A, **64**, 881.

23. KUSHNERIUK, S. A., and MCKAY, C. (July 1954). Canadian *A.E.C.L. Report*, CRT-566.
24. SELENGUT, D. S. (1958). Nuclear Physics Research Quarterly Report. Hanford Laboratories, HW-59126.
25. PLACZEK, G. (1946). *Phys. Rev.*, **69**, 423.
26. SPINNEY, K. T. (1957). *Journal of Nuclear Energy*, **6**, 53.
27. CHRISTY, R. F., WEINBERG, A. M., and WIGNER, E. P. (1944). U.S. Report, CP-2062.
28. GUREVICH, I., and POMERANCHOUK, I. Y. (1955). *Proceedings of the First International Conference on the Peaceful Uses of Atomic Energy*. Geneva Paper 649.
29. WIGNER, E. P., and WILKINS, J. E. (1944). U.S. Report, AECD-2275.
30. WILKINS, J. E. (1944). American Report, CP-2481.
31. SCHOFIELD, P. (1963). A.E.R.E. Report, T.P. 99.
32. NELKIN, M. (June 1960). *Nuclear Science and Engineering*, **7**, No. 6.
33. KLADNICK, R., and KUSCER, I. (1961). *Nuclear Science and Engineering*, **11**, No. 6.
34. WALLER, I. (1947). *Ark. Mat. Astr. Fys.*, **34A**, Nos. 3 to 5.
35. WICK, G. C. (1949). *Phys. Rev.*, **75**, 738.
36. VERDE, M., and WICK, G. C. (1947). *Phys. Rev.*, **71**, 852.
37. GOLDSTEIN, H., (1959). *Fundamental Aspects of Reactor Shielding*. Addison Wesley Publishing Company.
38. PRICE, B. T., HORTON, C. C., and SPINNEY, K. T. (1957). *Radiation Shielding*, Pergamon Press.
39. SAMPSON, J. B., and CHERNICK, J. (1958). *Prog. in Nuclear Energy, Physics and Mathematics*, **2**, 223 (Pergamon Press).
40. MEYER, M. A. (1956). *Symposium on Monte Carlo Methods*, Wiley.
41. HAMMERSLEY, J. M., and MORTON, K. W. (1956). *Proc. Camb. Phil. Soc.*, **52**, 449.
42. CARLSON, B. G. (1955). Los Alamos Scientific Laboratory Report, LA-1891.
43. CARLSON, B. G. (1959). Los Alamos Scientific Laboratory Report, LA-2260.
44. CARLSON, B. G., LEE, C., and WORLTON, J. (1959). Los Alamos Scientific Laboratory Report, LA-2346.
45. ACKROYD, R. T., and PENDLEBURY, E. D. (1961). *Survey of Theoretical Calculation Methods*. Karlsruhe Symposium on

Criticality Control in Chemical and Metallurgical Plant. Published by the European Nuclear Energy Agency.

46. MANDL, M. E. (1954). Harwell Report, A.E.R.E. T/R1500.

47. EHRLICH, R., and HURWITZ, H. (1954). *Nucleonics*, **12**, Nos. 2, 23.

48. MANDL, M. E., and HOWLETT, J. (1955). *Proceedings of the First International Conference on the Peaceful Uses of Atomic Energy*, Geneva Paper 433.

49. FUCHS, K. (1949). *Proc. Phys. Soc.*, **62**A, 791.

50. GLASSTONE, S., and EDLUND, M. C. (1952). *The Elements of Nuclear Reactor Theory*, Van Nostrand.

51. TAIT, J. H. (1954). *Proc. Phys. Soc.*, **67**A, 615.

52. PENDLEBURY, E. D. (1958). *Proc. Phys. Soc.*, **68**A, 474.

53. PARKER, K. (1961). Aldermaston Report, AWRE 0-1/61.

54. YIFTAH, S., OKRENT, D., and MOLAUER, P. A. (1960). *Fast Reactor Cross Sections*. Pergamon Press.

55. ROWLANDS, G. (1961). *Journal of Nuclear Energy*, Part A: Reactor Science, **13**, 176.

56. WATSON, G. N. (1944). *A Treatise on the Theory of Bessel Functions*. Cambridge University Press.

57. CASE, K. M. (1960) *Annals of Physics*, **91**, No. 1.

INDEX